Bond

Verbal Reasoning
Assessment Papers

10–11+ years
Book 2

Jane Bayliss

Published in 2007 by:
Nelson Thornes Ltd
Delta Place
27 Bath Road
CHELTENHAM
GL53 7TH
United Kingdom

12 / 2

A catalogue record for this book is available from the British Library

ISBN 978 1 4085 1623 2

Page make-up by Tech Set Ltd

Printed and bound in Egypt by Sahara Printing Company

Before you get started

What is Bond?

This book is part of the Bond Assessment Papers series for verbal reasoning, which provides a **thorough and progressive course in verbal reasoning** from ages six to twelve. It builds up verbal reasoning skills from book to book over the course of the series.

Bond's verbal reasoning resources are ideal preparation for the 11+ and other secondary school selection exams.

How does the scope of this book match real exam content?

Verbal Reasoning 10–11+ Book 1 and *Book 2* are the core Bond 11+ books. Each paper is **pitched at the level of a typical 11+ exam** and practises a wide range of questions drawn from the four distinct groups of verbal reasoning question types: sorting words, selecting words, anagrams, coded sequences and logic. The papers are fully in line with 11+ and other selective exams for this age group but are designed to practise **a wider variety of skills and question types** than most other practice papers so that children are always challenged to think – and don't get bored repeating the same question type again and again. We believe that variety is the key to effective learning. It helps children 'think on their feet' and cope with the unexpected: it is surprising how often children come out of verbal reasoning exams having met question types they have not seen before.

What does the book contain?

- **13 papers** – each one contains 80 questions.
- **Tutorial links throughout** – 📖 – this icon appears in the margin next to the questions. It indicates links to the relevant section in *How to do … 11+ Verbal Reasoning*, our invaluable subject guide that offers explanations and practice for all core question types.
- **Scoring devices** – there are score boxes in the margins and a Progress Chart on page 60. The chart is a visual and motivating way for children to see how they are doing. It also turns the score into a percentage that can help you decide what to do next.
- **Next Steps Planner** – advice on what to do after finishing the papers can be found on the inside back cover.
- **Answers** – located in an easily-removed central pull-out section.

How can you use this book?

One of the great strengths of Bond Assessment Papers is their flexibility. They can be used at home, in school and by tutors to:

- set **timed formal practice tests** – allow about 45 minutes per paper in line with standard 11+ demands. Reduce the suggested time limit by five minutes to practise working at speed.

- provide **bite-sized chunks** for regular practice
- **highlight strengths and weaknesses** in the core skills
- identify **individual needs**
- set **homework**
- follow **a complete 11+ preparation strategy** alongside *The Parents' Guide to the 11+* (see below).

It is best to start at the beginning and work through the papers in order. If you are using the book as part of a careful run-in to the 11+, we suggest that you also have two other essential Bond resources close at hand:

How to do ... 11+ Verbal Reasoning: the subject guide that explains all the question types practised in this book. Use the cross-reference icons to find the relevant sections.

The Parents' Guide to the 11+: the step-by-step guide to the whole 11+ experience. It clearly explains the 11+ process, provides guidance on how to assess children, helps you to set complete action plans for practice and explains how you can use *Verbal Reasoning 10–11+ Book 1* and *Book 2* as part of a strategic run-in to the exam.

See the inside front cover for more details of these books.

What does a child's score mean and how can it be improved?

It is unfortunately impossible to guarantee that a child will pass the 11+ exam if they achieve a certain score on any practice book or paper. Success on the day depends on a host of factors, including the scores of the other children sitting the test. However, we can give some guidance on what a score indicates and how to improve it.

If children colour in the Progress Chart on page 60, this will give an idea of present performance in percentage terms. The Next Steps Planner inside the back cover will help you to decide what to do next to help a child progress. It is always valuable to go over wrong answers with children. If they are having trouble with any particular question type, follow the tutorial links to *How to do ... 11+ Verbal Reasoning* for step-by-step explanations and further practice.

Don't forget the website...!

Visit www.bond11plus.co.uk for lots of advice, information and suggestions on everything to do with Bond, the 11+ and helping children to do their best.

Find and underline the two words which need to change places for each sentence to make sense. `B 17`

    Example   She went to <u>letter</u> the <u>write</u>.

1 The <u>queue</u> to the museum stood in the <u>visitors.</u>

2 <u>Not</u> had <u>she</u> packed a lunch.

3 Most <u>bones</u> like <u>dogs</u>.

4 I ran upstairs <u>get</u> <u>to</u> my book.

5 <u>Out</u> jumped <u>he</u> of the tree.   (5) `5`

Underline one word in the brackets which is most opposite in meaning to the word in capitals. `B 6`

    Example   WIDE   (broad vague long <u>narrow</u> motorway)

6 APPEAR   (look image <u>vanish</u> seem arrival)

7 SILENT   (quiet shy peaceful <u>noisy</u> still)

8 RISE   (grow <u>descend</u> slope raise position)

9 PLAIN   (flat <u>fancy</u> simple ugly clear)

10 RUNNY   (flowing <u>solid</u> stream dashing liquid)   (5) `5`

11–15 Look at these groups of words. `B 1`

A	B	C	D
hamster	peach	tennis	cod
elephant	plum	cricket	haddock

  Choose the correct group for each of the words below. Write in the letter.

trout _D_   kiwi _B_   rounders _C_ cheetah _A_ plaice _D_

satsuma _B_ weasel _A_ salmon _D_ lacrosse _C_ badminton _C_   (5) `5`

Underline two words, one from each group, that go together to form a new word. The word in the first group always comes first. `B 8`

    Example   (hand, <u>green</u>, for)   (light, <u>house</u>, sure)

16 (moth, <u>ant</u>, frog)   (hop, <u>eater</u>, tick)

17 (cut, <u>pen</u>, write)   (pencil, ink, <u>knife</u>)

18 (more, make, <u>need</u>)   (want, <u>less</u>, done)

19 (<u>friend</u>, sea, wreck)   (best, kind, <u>ship</u>)

20 (fox, skip, <u>broad</u>)   (den, <u>cast</u>, rope)   (5) `5`

Underline the pair of words most similar in meaning.

Example   come, go   <u>roam, wander</u>   fear, fare

21 ~~night, dawn~~   seldom, often   <u>guess, suspect</u>

22 ~~hand, foot~~   <u>option, choice</u>   few, many

23 <u>diminish, lessen</u>   proceed, stop   absence, presence

24 ~~near, far~~   <u>ruler, controller</u>   need, wish

25 ~~dog, pet~~   solid, hollow   <u>job, task</u>

B 5

5 5

Andy and Christine like tennis.
Brian and Christine like football, but not swimming.
Only Daxa likes tennis and swimming.

26 Which sport is most popular? __tennis__

B 25

1 1

If A = 2, B = 4, C = 5 and D = 6:

Give the answers to each of these calculations as a letter.

27 $(D - B) \times A =$ B

28 $D + B - C =$ C

29 $(A \times B) \div B =$ ~~A~~

B 26

3 3

Fill in the crosswords so that all the given words are included. You have been given one letter as a clue in each crossword.

B 19

30–31

~~alert~~
~~latch~~
~~angel~~
~~grace~~
~~teeth~~
~~enact~~

32–33
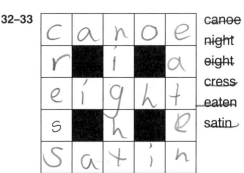

~~canoe~~
~~night~~
~~eight~~
~~cress~~
~~eaten~~
~~satin~~

4 4

Fill in the missing letters. The alphabet has been written out to help you.

A B C D E F G H I J K L M N O P Q R S T U V W X Y Z

Example   AB is to CD as PQ is to RS

34 CD is to EF as IJ is to ~~KI~~ KL

35 FH is to HG as MO is to ON

36 XV is to UY as JH is to GK

37 RN is to SO as BD is to CE

38 AD is to ZW as CF is to XU

B 23

5 5

If * ^ % £ ! ^ ~ # is the code for H O M E W O R K, what are the codes for these words?

(handwritten above code: H o m e w o r k)

39 MORE   % ^ ~ £

40 WORM   ! ^ ~ %

41 MEEK   % ££ #

42 WHERE   ! * £ ~ £

43 ROOM   ~ ^ ^ %

Laura, Omar, James, Kate, Eva and Jacob are six children. Omar is older than Kate, but younger than Laura. James is the oldest child and Eva is not the youngest. Kate is older than just two children.

List the children in order of age, starting with the oldest.

44 Jame

45 Laura

46 Omar

47 Kate

48 Eva

49 Jacob

Give the two missing numbers in the following sequences.

	Example	2	4	6	8	10	12
50	16	13	17	14	18	15	
51	3	6	12	24	48	96	
52	2	3	5	6	8	9	
53	7	9	12	16	21	27	
54	5	1	10	2	15	3	

Find the letter which will end the first word and start the second word.

Example   peac (h) ome

55 pos (t) rip

56 wor (m) oan

57 war (t) haw

58 lic (e) ase

59 her (d) amp

Change the first word into the last word, by changing one letter at a time and making a new, different word in the middle.

Example   CASE   _CASH_   LASH

60 STOP   _Step_   STEM

61 LOVE   _live_   GIVE

62 JEER   ~~Deaf~~   DEAR _Deer_

63 BAIT   _Bail_   PAIL

64 CRAB   _Grab_   GRUB

Underline the one word in the brackets which will go equally well with both the pairs of words outside the brackets.

Example   rush, attack   cost, fee   (price, hasten, strike, <u>charge</u>, money)

65 regarding, concerning   roughly, nearly   (refer, close, <u>about</u>, almost, talking)

66 unlocked, unfastened   start, launch   (gaping, place, <u>open</u>, shut, begin)

67 break, crack   bite, nip   (quick, <u>snap</u>, twig, burst, sharp)

68 faded, dim   collapse, black out   (dizzy, light, sick, <u>faint</u>, dull)

69 annoyed, grumpy   circle, square   (shape, angry, <u>cross</u>, diamond, cut)

Read the first two statements and then underline one of the four options below that must be true.

70 'Chairs are furniture. Furniture can be made of wood.'

       Trees supply wood.

       Wood is used for all furniture.

       <u>Chairs can be made of wood.</u>

       Trees are furniture because they are wood.

Find the four-letter word hidden at the end of one word and the beginning of the next word. The order of the letters may not be changed.

Example   The children had bats and balls.   _sand_

71 If you blow and blow the candle will go out.   _wand_

72 The argument began when Laurie took Jenna's pen.   _hear_

73 Each opponent must weigh in first.   _Chop_

74 Will you help me find one that isn't broken.   _done_

75 The rabbits stayed quite still as we passed.   _test_

Underline the one word which **cannot be made** from the letters of the word in capital letters.

Example   STATIONERY   stone   tyres   ration   <u>nation</u>   noisy

76 DIGESTION   signet   onset   <u>notice</u>   tides   stone

77 INTENSIVE   tense   sieve   veins   events   <u>nineteen</u>

78 UNDERNEATH   tender   earth   turned   ~~dated~~   heated

79 THURSDAY   shard   dusty   thuds   rusty   <u>hurry</u>

80 ANSWERED   swear   <u>drawer</u>   snared   swede   waned

 S 5

Now go to the Progress Chart to record your score!   Total 80 80

Paper 2

Give the two missing numbers in the following sequences.

Example   2   4   6   8   <u>10</u>   <u>12</u>

1   63   *56*   49   42   35   *28* ✓

2   4   8   *16*   32   64   *128* ✓

3   19   *17*   15   *13*   11   9 ✓

4   12   14   *17*   19   22   *24* ✓

5   27   24   23   *20*   19   *16* ✓

S 5

In 3 years' time Sarah will be twice as old as Emma was last year. Emma is now 11.

6 How old is Sarah now?   *17* ✓

/ 1

Here are the number codes for four words. Match the right word to the right code.

WALL	LAMP	MALE	PALE
5274	3255	4256	7256

7 WALL   *5274* ✗   *3255*

8 LAMP   *3255* ✗   *5274*

9 MALE   *4256* ✗   *7256*

10 PALE   *7256* ✗   *4256*

11 Write the code for LEAP.   *5624* ✓

/ 5

Complete the following sentences in the best way by choosing one word from each set of brackets.

Example Tall is to (tree, short, colour) as narrow is to (thin, white, wide).

12 Horse is to (foal, stable, saddle) as cow is to (milk, grass, calf). ✓

13 Car is to (petrol, speed, driver) as aeroplane is to (pilot, holiday, airport). ✓

14 Hurry is to (hasten, slow, move) as assemble is to (school, repeat, gather). ✓

15 Match is to (burn, stick, game) as head is to (hair, body, boss). ✓

16 Spring is to (summer, season, jump) as march is to (calendar, walk, winter) ✓

5 5

Rearrange the muddled letters in capitals to make a proper word. The answer will complete the sentence sensibly.

Example A BEZAR is an animal with stripes. ZEBRA

17 Look right and left before you SORCS the road. Cross

18 Katie enjoyed her summer YHLADOI. Holiday

19 He used the LERUR to underline the title. Ruler

20 She hurt her STRIW. Wrist

21 The whole class went to the YAPTR. Party

5 5

Underline the one word in the brackets which will go equally well with both the pairs of words outside the brackets.

Example rush, attack   cost, fee   (price, hasten, strike, charge, money)

22 end, point   empty, pour out ✓ (nib, spill, tip, rubbish, top)

23 bounce, leap   leave out, miss ✓ (jump, try, ball, skip, forget)

24 guide, teach   performance, act ✓ (parade, explain, show, amuse, lead)

25 location, area   arrange, put ✓ (spot, flowers, live, place, keep)

26 document, folder   note, store ✓ (notice, paper, file, remark, keep)

5 5

Find the four-letter word hidden at the end of one word and the beginning of the next word. The order of the letters may not be changed.

Example The children had bats and balls. sand

27 I wish all my friends lived near me. hall

28 The squid lay its tentacle over yellow weed. very

29 My cousin wants to be an electrician. bean

30 Pigs eat different sorts of scraps. seat

31 Here are the keys to the car. rear

5 5

Complete the following sentences by selecting the most sensible word from each group of words given in the brackets. Underline the words selected.

Example The (<u>children</u>, books, foxes) carried the (houses, <u>books</u>, steps) home from the (greengrocer, <u>library</u>, factory).

32 The (<u>girl</u>, puppy, toy) asked her (toy, <u>mother</u>, bone) for some (rain, shops, <u>sweets</u>).

33 Remember to (cross, ask, <u>check</u>) your (<u>work</u>, friend, breakfast) before handing it to the (dentist, <u>teacher</u>, waiter).

34 They enjoy (skipping, <u>riding</u>, swimming) their (<u>horses</u>, boats, fish) in the (playground, <u>field</u>, pitch).

35 Mix the (bowl, <u>butter</u>, kitchen) with the (<u>sugar</u>, mustard, medicine), then add some (detergent, powder, <u>eggs</u>).

36 The weather was (foggy, <u>sunny</u>, frosty) and too (easy, moody, <u>hot</u>) to play on the (<u>beach</u>, circus, cinema).

Underline two words, one from each group, that go together to form a new word. The word in the first group always comes first.

Example (hand, <u>green</u>, for) (light, <u>house</u>, sure)

37 (small, <u>cross</u>, draw) (shout, shape, <u>roads</u>)

38 (share, <u>cap</u>, telephone) (<u>size</u>, cause, ring)

39 (<u>use</u>, beauty, me) (full, <u>less</u>, all)

40 (grass, <u>sea</u>, shine) (sun, bright, <u>weed</u>)

41 (go, <u>near</u>, walk) (close, far, <u>by</u>)

Move one letter from the first word and add it to the second word to make two new words.

Example hunt sip <u>hut</u> <u>snip</u>

42 climb rack *limb* *crack*

43 forty part *fort* *party*

44 splay crumb *play* *crumbs*

45 ruin deal *run* *ideal*

46 thrust sore *trust* *shore*

Underline the two words, one from each group, which are closest in meaning.

Example (race, shop, <u>start</u>) (finish, <u>begin</u>, end)

47 (<u>calm</u>, sea, cool) (wind, <u>still</u>, waves)

48 (sun, <u>beam</u>, star) (hot, <u>shine</u>, sky)

49 (dog, <u>scratch</u>, claw) (<u>graze</u>, knee, sore)

50 (<u>fair</u>, rich, dark) (poor, <u>honest</u>, reliable)

51 (hit, fall, <u>force</u>) (hand, <u>power</u>, fail)

Find the letter which will end the first word and start the second word.

Example   peac (h) ome

52 note (d) eaf ✓

53 jump (s) hape ✓

54 rai (d) aft ✓

55 kne (w) ide ✓

56 fro (g) lee ✓

5 5

Find the three-letter word which can be added to the letters in capitals to make a new word. The new word will complete the sentence sensibly.

Example   The cat sprang onto the MO.   USE

57 He ate fish and CS in the café.   hip

58 The NOT appeared in the newspaper.   ice

59 I helped my mother with the SPING.   hop

60 Try to LN your spellings in time for the test.   ear

61 The car SPED at the traffic lights.   top

B 22

5 5

Fill in the crosswords so that all the given words are included. You have been given one letter as a clue in each crossword.

62–63

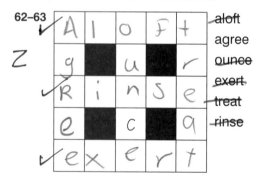

aloft
agree
ounce
exert
treat
rinse

64–65

sandy
acorn
socks
choir
stamp
party

B 19

4 4

Give the missing groups of letters in the following sequences. The alphabet has been written out to help you.

A B C D E F G H I J K L M N O P Q R S T U V W X Y Z

66 ZA   YB   XC   WD   E   UF

67 CA   EC   GE   IG   KI   MK

68 VAJ   WBK   XCL   YDM   ZEN   AFO

69 AT   DR   GP   JN   ML   PJ

70 PA   BQ   RC   DS   TE   FU

B 23

5 5

8

If P = 6, Q = 4, R = 2, S = 12 and T = 8:

B 26

Give the answer to each of these calculations as a letter.

71 P + Q + R = _S_ ✓

72 (Q × Q) − (P − R) = _S_ ✓ _P_

73 Q × R = _T_ ✓

74 S ÷ R = ___

75 (R × T) ÷ Q = _Q_ ✓

S 5

Which one letter can be added to the front of all of these words to make new words?

B 12

	Example	care	cat	crate	call
76	_b_owl	_b_one	_b_reak	_b_ray	_b_rain
77	_J_am	_J_oint	_J_ump	_J_ust	_J_ewel
78	_F_ront	_F_oil	_F_lower	_F_orce	_F_ool
79	_N_ake	_N_ait	_N_eed	_N_ild	_N_hat
80	_W_ear	_W_ame	_W_eigh	_W_est	_W_ose

3 5

75 ✓

Now go to the Progress Chart to record your score!   Total 76 80

Paper 3

Look at these groups of words.

B 1

A	B	C
Trees	Food	Birds

Choose the correct group for each of the words below. Write in the letter.

1–5 parrot ___   pine ___   broccoli ___   willow ___   eagle ___

beans ___   noodles ___   wren ___   robin ___   oak ___

5

Underline the two words which are the odd ones out in the following groups of words.

B 4

	Example	black	king	purple	green	house
6	idea	thought	clever		notion	dull
7	divide	join	subtract		unite	combine
8	nearby	remote	neighbouring		foreign	distant
9	compel	lively	force		pressure	sad
10	hint	lie	complaint		sign	indication

5

Find the letter which will end the first word and start the second word.

B 10

Example   peac (<u>h</u>) ome

11 mos (___) alt

12 jum (___) lum

13 gla (___) eck

14 sol (___) nion

15 win (___) nit

5

Complete the following sentences by selecting the most sensible word from each group of words given in the brackets. Underline the words selected.

B 14

Example   The (<u>children</u>, books, foxes) carried the (houses, <u>books</u>, steps) home from the (greengrocer, <u>library</u>, factory).

16 We all need (books, food, soap) to help build a (healthy, cold, solid) (garden, air, body).

17 A (lion, giraffe, crocodile) can eat the (leaves, rice, meat) from the (highest, fastest, tidiest) part of the tree.

18 Never (fly, sing, stand) under a (tree, bird, aeroplane) during a thunderstorm.

19 He left after (lunch, breakfast, midnight) on a (rainy, summery, hot) November (year, night, Christmas).

20 She (took, removed, put) her (muddy, shiny, laces) shoes before walking on the new (sand, grass, carpet).

5

Underline the pair of words most opposite in meaning.

B 9

Example   cup, mug   coffee, milk   <u>hot, cold</u>

21 danger, risk   notice, remark   guilty, innocent

22 exact, true   slow, swift   connect, link

23 joy, sorrow   uncover, open   mistake, error

24 floppy, hanging   hazard, safety   alike, same

25 accurate, wrong   roomy, spacious   lap, circuit

5

Complete the following expressions by filling in the missing word.

B 15

Example   Pen is to ink as brush is to <u>paint</u>.

26 Mother is to father as _____ is to son.

27 Century is to hundred as dozen is to _____.

28 Find is to fine as mind is to _____.

29 Flock is to sheep as _____ is to cows.

30 January is to December as Tuesday is to _____.

5

Find a word that can be put in front of each of the following words to make new, compound words.

	Example	CAST	FALL	WARD	POUR	DOWN
31	BOAT	BUOY	GUARD	JACKET		_____
32	GAP	OVER	WATCH	PAGE		_____
33	GUARD	FIGHTER	FLY	POWER		_____
34	WORK	LAND	PECKER	WORM		_____
35	ACHE	STROKE	WARD	DATE		_____

 5

Underline the one word in the brackets which will go equally well with both the pairs of words outside the brackets.

Example   rush, attack   cost, fee   (price, hasten, strike, <u>charge</u>, money)

36   ice, chill   stop, standstill   (cold, fix, freeze, wintry, halt)

37   team, gang   edge, margin   (party, side, limit, area, support)

38   boring, uninteresting   gloomy, cloudy   (clear, weather, exciting, dull, work)

39   here, attending   gift, donation   (guest, charity, ready, present, show)

40   find, hunt   path, trail   (train, track, sniff, catch, line)

 5

Thomas, Kasim, Charlotte and Elena all have sandwiches in their lunchboxes.
Most of the children prefer healthy snacks.
Elena has a pear and Kasim has an apple.
Thomas, Charlotte and Elena have yogurts.
Elena was running late for school and is the only child who has forgotten to bring a drink.
Kasim has a snack bar in case he still feels hungry.

41   How many children have sandwiches, yogurt and a drink for lunch?   _____

42   Which two children have the same items for lunch?   _____

43   Which child has the most items in their lunchbox?   _____

 3

Fill in the crosswords so that all the given words are included. You have been given one letter as a clue in each crossword.

44–45

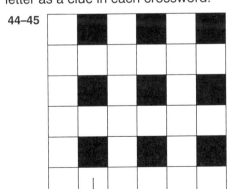

stamps, angers, disuse, nested, extend, timber

46–47

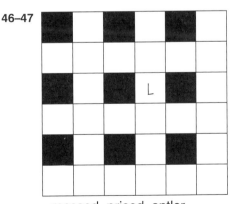

messed, prised, antler, pilots, inside, floods

4

If < £ > < / ? $ £ is the code for SENSIBLE what do these codes stand for?

48 < £ > < £   _____

49 $ / > £   _____

50 $ £ < <   _____

What are the codes for the following words?

51 BINS   _____

52 BLISS   _____

Give the two missing numbers in the following sequences.

Example		2	4	6	8	10	12

53	17	21	___	29	___	37
54	15	___	20	18	___	27
55	96	48	24	12	___	___
56	47	___	41	38	35	___
57	14	23	33	___	56	___

modem   monster   model   mould   mobile

If these words were placed in alphabetical order, which word would come:

58 second?   _____

59 last?   _____

60 first?   _____

Find the four-letter word hidden at the end of one word and the beginning of the next word. The order of the letters may not be changed.

Example   The children had bats and balls.   _sand_

61 Sometimes I wash old golf balls then resell them.   _____

62 Some of the buses went on but mine stopped at the corner.   _____

63 We are going to paint your room this weekend.   _____

64 The missing cat eventually came home.   _____

65 Everyone at my office begins at nine.   _____

Rearrange the muddled letters in capitals to make a proper word. The answer will complete the sentence sensibly.

Example   A BEZAR is an animal with stripes.   _ZEBRA_

66–67 They climbed the ERET at the TTMOOB of the garden.   _____   _____

68 Dark clouds usually bring IANR.   _____

69–70 Switch your THILG off by NENI.   _____   _____

Underline the one word which **cannot be made** from the letters of the word in capital letters.

B 7

	Example	STATIONERY	stone	tyres	ration	<u>nation</u>	noisy
71	DESCRIPTION		cried	snort	nicer	pride	preen
72	BREAKDOWN		brand	wander	dream	rowed	brown
73	PLASTERING		staring	string	laser	grass	strain
74	BANNISTER		banter	stern	nasty	rinse	tribe
75	SILHOUETTE		house	those	teeth	heels	honest

5

Find the three-letter word which can be added to the letters in capitals to make a new word. The new word will complete the sentence sensibly.

B 22

Example The cat sprang onto the MO. <u>USE</u>

76 On Saturday they went to the nursery to buy some PLS. _____

77 She only managed to write a couple of SENCES. _____

78 Take that out of your MH! _____

79 The audience CPED enthusiastically. _____

80 SHAR your pencils please. _____

5

Now go to the Progress Chart to record your score! **Total** 80

Paper 4

Underline two words, one from each group, that go together to form a new word. The word in the first group always comes first.

B 8

Example (hand, <u>green</u>, for) (light, <u>house</u>, sure)

1 (birthday, card, best) (week, fun, board)

2 (we, his, my) (sister, self, own)

3 (no, yes, nice) (thanks, there, thing)

4 (bread, butter, knife) (cup, fork, spread)

5 (rug, mat, go) (door, by, stick)

5

Add one letter to the word in capital letters to make a new word. The meaning of the new word is given in the clue.

B 12

Example   PLAN   simple   <u>plain</u>

6 PIECE   make a hole   _____

7 FIN   not rainy   _____

8 ONE   on one occasion   _____

9 LOSE   unfastened   _____

10 MAN   unkind   _____

5

Underline the one word in the brackets which will go equally well with both the pairs of words outside the brackets.

B 5

Example   rush, attack   cost, fee   (price, hasten, strike, <u>charge</u>, money)

11 club, diamond   hoe, rake   (weapon, spade, jewel, garden, heart)

12 bracelet, necklace   telephone, bell   (wedding, ring, line, valuable, rich)

13 toss, throw   actors, players   (grab, role, project, catch, cast)

14 cosy, at ease   well-off, wealthy   (easy, rich, comfortable, helpful, happy)

15 decrease, reduce   ignore, unimportant   (share, sale, allow, discount, bother)

5

Underline the two words which are the odd ones out in the following groups of words.

B 4

Example   black   <u>king</u>   purple   green   <u>house</u>

16 run   trainer   walk   sock   jog

17 hot   roast   grill   spicy   toast

18 plan   idea   organize   drawing   prepare

19 cub   cat   gosling   lamb   goat

20 orange   brown   grass   lemon   cherry

5

Alice catches the bus at 7:15 am and arrives at her destination 1 hour 30 minutes later.
Her journey takes twice as long as Grace's.
Lucy's bus leaves at 7:45 am and her journey takes 20 minutes.
Grace's bus leaves at 7:30 am.

B 25

21 At what time does Alice complete her journey?   _____

22 At what time does Grace's bus reach its destination?   _____

23 At what time does Lucy's journey end?   _____

3

14

Give the two missing numbers in the following sequences.

B 23

    Example   2   4   6   8   <u>10</u>   <u>12</u>

24 17 ____ ____ 23 25 27

25 11 14 22 16 ____ ____

26 ____ 4 6 9 13 ____

27 19 22 24 ____ ____ 32

28 ____ 5 3 ____ 4 15

5

Find the three-letter word which can be added to the letters in capitals to make a new word. The new word will complete the sentence sensibly.

B 22

    Example   The cat sprang onto the MO.   <u>USE</u>

29 She FED her mug with tea.   _____

30 When it's hot, my dog lies in the SE.   _____

31 Children usually prefer SY beaches.   _____

32 SUDLY, I wanted to go.   _____

33 The book is on the SH.   _____

5

Underline the pair of words most opposite in meaning.

B 9

    Example   cup, mug   coffee, milk   <u>hot, cold</u>

34 forest, wood   true, false,   mild, gentle

35 student, pupil   car, auto   rear, front

36 visit, call   cheeky, polite   child, infant

37 allow, deny   marry, join   dig, burrow

38 change, swap   same, alike   total, partial

5

Find the letter which will end the first word and start the second word.

B 10

    Example   peac (<u>h</u>) ome

39 luc (____) iss

40 bul (____) ell

41 gro (____) asp

42 fol (____) erb

43 oa (____) race

5

Read the first two statements and then underline one of the four options below that must be true.

B 25

  44 'Fish breathe underwater. Goldfish are a common type of pet fish.'

      Goldfish make good pets.

      The seas are full of fish.

      Goldfish breathe underwater.

      Fish live in salt water.

Read the first two statements and then underline one of the four options below that must be true.

45 'Bees make honey. Honey tastes sweet.'

Bees are sweet.

Everyone likes honey.

Bees make sweet honey.

Bees can sting.

Read the first two statements and then underline one of the four options below that must be true.

46 'Some shoes are made from leather. Leather is waterproof.'

Shoes are worn with socks.

All shoes are made from leather.

Leather shoes are waterproof.

Leather is the best material for shoes.

3

Fill in the crosswords so that all the given words are included. You have been given one letter as a clue in each crossword.

B 19

47–48

better, cheeky, trying, yogurt, exists, hordes

49–50

litter, glides, recede, strain, drawer, sunset

4

Fill in the missing letters. The alphabet has been written out to help you.

B 23

A B C D E F G H I J K L M N O P Q R S T U V W X Y Z

Example   AB is to CD as PQ is to R*S*

51 CN is to DO as HR is to   ____

52 HF is to JD as MW is to   ____

53 CBE is to DAF as PNS is to   ____

54 BD is to EG as RT is to   ____

55 LCF is to KBE as TXQ is to   ____

5

knead   knight   knick   kneeing   kneecap

If these words were put in alphabetical order, which one would come:

56 third? _____

57 fourth? _____

If the words were listed in reverse in alphabetical order, which one would come:

58 first? _____

59 last? _____

60 fourth? _____

5

If ? & $ * ! £ @ > < is the code for COMPUTERS, what do these codes stand for?

61 < £ & > @   _____

62 $ & < £   _____

63 ? & ! > < @   _____

What are the codes for the following words?

64 TERM   _____

65 CUTE   _____

5

Underline the two words which are made from the same letters.

	Example	TAP	PET	<u>TEA</u>	POT	<u>EAT</u>
66	NAME	AMEND	DREAM	MEAN	MADE	NEAR
67	TAPS	STARE	SNAP	TAPE	PANT	PANS
68	MILLS	MILES	SLIME	SAWN	WARM	WORM
69	MARCH	CHANT	WEAR	CHARM	WATCH	MARSH
70	SEVEN	PHRASE	SHAPE	GRAPH	PHASE	SEVER

5

Find and underline the two words which need to change places for each sentence to make sense.

Example   She went to <u>letter</u> the <u>write</u>.

71 Dad drives to us school in the car.

72 She had knee her cut badly.

73 I have to wait and sit.

74 Mum knows we trick planning to were her.

75 We cash to the bank to get some went.

5

17

If s = 3, e = 2, r = 5, a = 1, t = 6 and d = 4, find the value of the following words by adding the letters together.

B 26

76 rested   _____

77 read   _____

78 treat   _____

79 stared   _____

80 deer   _____

       5

Now go to the Progress Chart to record your score!   **Total**   80

Paper 5

Remove one letter from the word in capital letters to leave a new word. The meaning of the new word is given in the clue.

B 12

Example   AUNT   an insect   <u>ant</u>

1 DOZEN   sleep   _____

2 TIRED   joined   _____

3 SPOUT   place   _____

4 BOUND   connection   _____

5 PLEASANT   bumpkin   _____

       5

Underline the two words, one from each group, which are closest in meaning.

B 3

Example   (race, shop, <u>start</u>)   (finish, <u>begin</u>, end)

6 (hit, punch, hand)   (success, fail, nervous)

7 (behave, complication, rule)   (quiz, mood, problem)

8 (cheap, price, buy)   (fee, purse, sell)

9 (mind, real, imagine)   (eye, suppose, copy)

10 (test, proof, try)   (lies, tell, evidence)

       5

Complete the following sentences by selecting the most sensible word from each group of words given in the brackets. Underline the words selected.

B 14

Example   The (<u>children</u>, books, foxes) carried the (houses, <u>books</u>, steps) home from the (greengrocer, <u>library</u>, factory).

11 She bought some (steak, flowers, tomatoes) from the (chemist, bank, butcher).

12 The boy had to (work, wait, cycle) in the (sea, farm, playground) because his mother was (late, happy, kind).

13 Be (brave, quick, quiet)! I can't (see, hear, feel) what they're (saying, thinking, learning).

14 We need a (dictionary, book, map) to (lose, find, view) our (car, way, photos).

15 (Cities, beaches, villages) are (repeatedly, weekly, often) full of tall (people, museums, buildings).

 5

Find the letter which will complete both pairs of words, ending the first word and starting the second. The same letter must be used for both pairs of words.

B 10

> **Example** mea (t) able   fi (t) ub

16 tria (——) ead   rea (——) ight

17 pla (——) es   tr   (——) ellow

18 brin (——) host   ran (——) rim

19 bul (——) lack   cri (——) ald

20 foo (——) emper   sal (——) hank

5

Underline the one word in the brackets which will go equally well with both the pairs of words outside the brackets.

B 5

> **Example** rush, attack   cost, fee   (price, hasten, strike, <u>charge</u>, money)

21 practise, rehearse   dig, pierce   (roll, drill, wind, turn, study)

22 oar, pole   dabble, splash   (steer, wade, waves, paddle, river)

23 review, inspect   stop, limit   (examine, check, confirm, halt, accept)

24 explode, roar   success, growth (thunder, echo, boom, crash, strong)

25 strength, energy   make, cause   (power, force, health, encourage, require)

5

Underline the one word which **cannot be made** from the letters of the word in capital letters.

B 7

> **Example** STATIONERY   stone   tyres   ration   <u>nation</u>   noisy

26 TELEPHONES   shone   pole   photo   honest   spent

27 STATUES   astute   suet   uses   sauce   states

28 PETRIFIES   fires   feast   spite   trees   rites

29 CHRISTMAS   smith   chasm   match   charm   start

30 RADISHES   shade   rashes   dress   shares   drains

5

19

Find a word that is similar in meaning to the word in capital letters and that rhymes with the second word.

Example   CABLE   tyre   <u>wire</u>

B 5

31   APPLAUD   strap   _____

32   ORDINARY   train   _____

33   BANQUET   least   _____

34   EMPLOY   choir   _____

35   LONGING   burn   _____

5

Find the four-letter word hidden at the end of one word and the beginning of the next word. The order of the letters may not be changed.

B 21

Example   The children had bats and balls.   <u>sand</u>

36   The clock struck twelve and minutes later we left.   _____

37   The best emeralds are used for jewellery.   _____

38   Some of his ideas were a bit unusual.   _____

39   Some people find it hard to admit when they are wrong.   _____

40   We made sure that no one missed their turn.   _____

5

Change the first word into the last word by changing one letter at a time and making a new, different word in the middle.

B 13

Example   CASE   <u>CASH</u>   LASH

41   WILL   _____   WIND

42   PITH   _____   WISH

43   HALL   _____   SALT

44   OXEN   _____   EVEN

45   KIND   _____   BAND

5

Complete the following expressions by underlining the missing word.

B 15

Example   Frog is to tadpole as swan is to (duckling, baby, <u>cygnet</u>).

46   Nimble is to agile as calm is to (excited, violent, still).

47   Soothe is to disturb as enjoy is to (adore, dislike, appreciate).

48   Grim is to pleasant as numerous is to (many, numbers, sparse).

49   Pleased is to delighted as greet is to (card, ignore, welcome).

50   Seldom is to often as descend is to (go, arrive, rise).

5

Fill in the crosswords so that all the given words are included. You have been given one
letter as a clue in each crossword.

51–52

simple, arrive, temple, cement
preens, aspect

53–54

adders, reveal, revert, revere
styles, beheld

55–56

nation, active, octave, finish
leaner, tether

Give the two missing numbers in the following sequences.

	Example	2	4	6	8	<u>10</u>	<u>12</u>
57	16	20	25	____	34	38	____
58	____	64	56	____	40	32	24
59	85	____	61	52	____	40	37
60	6	____	12	20	18	30	____

A B C D E F G H I J K L M N O P Q R S T U V W X Y Z

Solve the problems by working out the letter codes.

61 If the code for BEAT is CFBU, what is the code for MICE? _____

62 If the code for TEST is VGUV, what is the code for JUMP? _____

63 If the code for SKATE is RJZSD, what is the code for LINE? _____

64 If the code for CONSIDER is AMLQGBCP, what does
the code NSPQC stand for? _____

65 If the code for ALTER is BMUFS, what does the code ZPVOH stand for? _____

If A = 2, B = 4, C = 5, D = 10 and E = 8, give the answers to these calculations as letters.

B 26

66 B + E − A = _____

67 D × A ÷ B = _____

68 (E + B) − D = _____

69 C × A = _____

70 (D − B) + (E ÷ B) = _____

71 (B × A) − (A × A) = _____

6

Tom's hamster is 7 years younger than his cat. His dog, who is twice the age of the hamster, will be 7 next year.

B 25

72 How old is Tom's cat? _____

1

73 Write the letters of the word TADPOLE in the order in which they appear in the dictionary.

B 20

___ ___ ___ ___ ___ ___ ___

1

74 If the letters in the following word are arranged in alphabetical order, which letter comes in the middle?

B 20

MOVED ___

1

75 If the months of the year were arranged in alphabetical order, which month would come third?

B 20

_____

1

Spell the following words backwards. Write numbers underneath the words to indicate their new alphabetical order.

B 20

76 taught	thought	naughty	daughter
_____	_____	_____	_____
77 suit	fruit	juice	nuisance
_____	_____	_____	_____
78 fabulous	anxious	famous	enormous
_____	_____	_____	_____
79 illness	happiness	fitness	clumsiness
_____	_____	_____	_____
80 terrible	squirrel	horrible	wheel
_____	_____	_____	_____

5

Paper 6

B 23

Give the two missing pairs of letters in the following sequences. The alphabet has been written out to help you.

A B C D E F G H I J K L M N O P Q R S T U V W X Y Z

Example	CQ	DQ	EP	FP	_GO_	_HO_
1 ML	___	IH	GF	___	CB	
2 BC	DI	GN	___	PU	___	
3 AZ	___	EV	___	IR	KP	
4 KL	JM	___	HO	GP	___	
5 ZY	AB	XW	CD	___	___	

5

Fill in the crosswords so that all the given words are included. You have been given one letter as a clue in each crossword.

B 19

6–7

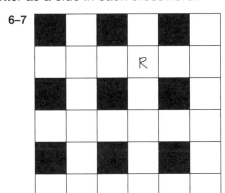

bearer, graded, eloped, triple, teller, friend

8–9

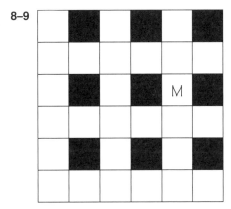

assume, banana, avenue, immune, ushers, answer

10–11

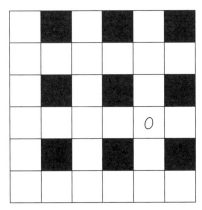

sunset, become, angles, needed, season, lesson

Find two letters which will end the first word and start the second word.

B 10

Example   rea (c h) air

12 nett   (—— ——) opard

13 roa   (—— ——) ing

14 form   (—— ——) rand

15 glo   (—— ——) ware

16 opti   (—— ——) ion   ○ 5

Complete the following sentences by selecting the most sensible word from each group of words given in the brackets. Underline the words selected.

B 14

Example   The (<u>children</u>, books, foxes) carried the (houses, <u>books</u>, steps) home from the (greengrocer, <u>library</u>, factory).

17 It was my (turn, problem, behaviour) to (swim, ride, walk) the (car, bike, trampoline).

18 We (picked, said, made) some (bread, strawberries, jam) in the (sand, river, field).

19 Please (wet, dry, dust) the (furniture, flowers, plates) before putting them in the (cupboard, case, wardrobe).

20 Wearing (trousers, goggles, boots) helps you to (swim, ride, trek) underwater.

21 I had to (complain, wonder, lie) about the (pleasant, exciting, loud) (treat, music, money) because it was keeping me awake.   ○ 5

Find the four-letter word hidden at the end of one word and the beginning of the next word. The order of these letters may not be changed.

B 21

Example   The children had bats and balls.   _sand_

22 Amy immediately posted her cards as she addressed them.   _____

23 William, please come at once.   _____

24 The sunset bathed the mountain in golden light.   _____   ○ 3

Underline the pair of words most similar in meaning.

B 5

Example   come, go   <u>roam, wander</u>   fear, fare

25 rapid, slow   hide, seek   abundant, plentiful

26 rare, common   answer, reply   prize, punishment

27 transcend, translate   nothing, everything   rhythm, beat

28 alter, change   lead, follow   protect, attack

29 costly, cheap   injury, damage   famous, unknown   ○ 5

Hannah and Charlie live in the country.

Charlie and Raj like going to the cinema.

Raj and Daisy live in a town and go to Drama Club.

30 Who lives in a town and likes going to the cinema? _____

If the code for PREVIOUS is 79643582, what do these codes stand for?

31 2896 _____

32 78926 _____

33 9576 _____

34 If the code for PRETEND is TUVWVYZ, what is the code for RENT? _____

35 If the code for SHADE is 24536, what word is 4653? _____

If S = 3, E = 2, R = 5, A = 1, T = 6 and D = 4, find the value of:

36 T + E + A = _____

37 (R × E) + (S × T) = _____

38 (S + T) − (A × R) = _____

39 (S × E) ÷ (A × T) = _____

40 Find the value of DRESSER by adding the letters together. _____

Find the three-letter word which can be added to the letters in capitals to make a new word. The new word will complete the sentence sensibly.

Example The cat sprang onto the MO. USE

41 My PNTS encourage me to play outside. _____

42–43 I packed lots of warm CLOS, but forgot my SPERS so my feet were cold.

_____ _____

44–45 The GES were fine but the bananas hadn't yet RIED. _____ _____

Underline the word in the brackets closest in meaning to the word in capitals.

Example UNHAPPY (unkind death laughter sad friendly)

46 COLLECTION (hobby scrapbook assortment interesting valuable)

47 COACH (trip driver school child instructor)

48 EXTERIOR (paint fence inside outside private)

49 STABLE (horses hay wobbly fixed shaky)

50 MIX (divide cake blend fork icing)

Change the first word into the last word by changing one letter at a time and making two new, different words in the middle.

B 13

Example   TEAK   _TEAT_   _TENT_   RENT

51 CALM   _____   _____   POLE

52 LARK   _____   _____   HAZE

53 WAIT   _____   _____   JARS

54 SITE   _____   _____   BILL

55 DOZE   _____   _____   MADE

5

Change one word so that the sentence makes sense. Underline the word you are taking out and write your new word on the line.

B 14

Example   I waited in line to buy a <u>book</u> to see the film.   _ticket_

56 You should always wear a safety cap when riding a bicycle.   _____

57 She put her car in the garden every night.   _____

58 Copy the poem again; your trying isn't neat enough.   _____

59 The moon was shining by midday, so he ate his lunch in the garden.   _____

60 We sit in the garden until dark during the long days of winter.   _____

5

Move one letter from the first word and add it to the second word to make two new words.

B 13

Example   hunt   sip   _hut_   _snip_

61 through   fog   _____   _____

62 boat   muse   _____   _____

63 tray   hem   _____   _____

64 blend   back   _____   _____

65 cheat   last   _____   _____

5

Find a word that can be put in front of each of the following words to make new, compound words.

B 11

Example   CAST   FALL   WARD   POUR   _DOWN_

66 SKIRTS   SIDE   LINE   BURST   _____

67 ON   DATE   ROAR   SET   _____

68 GO   TAKE   LINE   GROWTH   _____

69 SPOON   CAKE   TIME   CUP   _____

70 BOX   CARD   CODE   AGE   _____

5

Which word in each group contains only the first six letters of the alphabet?

	Example	defeat	farce	abide	<u>deaf</u>	dice

71	badge	deck	bead	beach	fake
72	cage	deal	cake	fade	beak
73	ease	debacle	decade	fable	each
74	cuff	bean	calf	bake	café
75	edge	fail	face	feel	edge

5

Look at these groups of words.

A	B	C
Clothing	Coast	Calendar

Choose the correct group for each of the words below. Write in the letter.

76–79   sand _____   diving _____   linen _____   cliffs _____

era _____   waistcoat _____   annual _____   monday _____

4

Read the first two statements and then underline one of the four options below that must be true.

80   'A monkey is an animal. Some monkeys live in the rainforests.'

Most monkeys live in rainforests.

A rainforest is a hot place.

Some animals live in rainforests.

Monkeys climb trees.

1

Now go to the Progress Chart to record your score!   Total   80

Paper 7

PROVOKE   PROVINCE   PROSPER   PROVISION   PROSPECT

If these words were placed in alphabetical order, which one would come:

1 first? _____

2 last? _____

3 middle? _____

4 fourth? _____

5 second? _____

5

Underline one word in the brackets which is most opposite in meaning to the word in capitals.

B 6

Example   WIDE   (broad   vague   long   <u>narrow</u>   motorway)

6   STALE   (bread   crisp   tasteless   flat   boring)

7   SPEAKER   (teacher   lawyer   politician   listener   leader)

8   BUSY   (active   routine   idle   occupied   service)

9   EXTEND   (build   reach   shorten   amount   line)

10   BREAK   (divide   limb   news   connect   fracture)

5

Find the three-letter word which can be added to the letters in capitals to make a new word. The new word will complete the sentence sensibly.

B 22

Example   The cat sprang onto the MO.   <u>USE</u>

11   She was DISTRED by the constant noise and found it hard to study.   _____

12   That's a BRIANT idea!   _____

13   I've THN my old shoes away.   _____

14   Why aren't you ALLD to come over?   _____

15   Let's grab a bite to eat BEE the film.   _____

5

Which one letter can be added to the front of all of these words on each line to make new words?

B 12

Example   _c_are   _c_at   _c_rate   _c_all

16   ___ife   ___ight   ___ice   ___oad   ___urk

17   ___ast   ___ine   ___ume   ___ield   ___ilm

18   ___ave   ___ear   ___ush   ___ort   ___aste

19   ___all   ___and   ___unch   ___ook   ___elm

20   ___able   ___ast   ___oast   ___old   ___ube

5

Move one letter from the first word and add it to the second word to make two new words.

B 13

Example   hunt   sip   <u>hut</u>   <u>snip</u>

21   fair   deal   _____   _____

22   chilly   earn   _____   _____

23   stage   suck   _____   _____

24   cover   dawn   _____   _____

25   feud   pond   _____   _____

5

Paper 1

1. queue, visitors
2. not, she
3. bones, dogs
4. get, to
5. out, he
6. vanish
7. noisy
8. descend
9. fancy
10. solid
11–15. trout D; satsuma B; kiwi B; weasel A; rounders C; salmon D; cheetah A; lacrosse C; plaice D; badminton C
16. anteater
17. penknife
18. needless
19. friendship
20. broadcast
21. guess, suspect
22. option, choice
23. diminish, lessen
24. ruler, controller
25. job, task
26. tennis
27. B
28. C
29. A
30–33. *Give two marks for each correct crossword.*

A	N	G	E	L
L		R		A
E	N	A	C	T
R		C		C
T	E	E	T	H

C	A	N	O	E
R		I		A
E	I	G	H	T
S		H		E
S	A	T	I	N

34. KL
35. ON
36. GK
37. CE
38. XU
39. % ^ ~ £
40. ! ^ ~ %
41. % £ £ #
42. ! * £ ~ £
43. ~ ^ ^ %
44. James
45. Laura
46. Omar
47. Kate
48. Eva
49. Jacob
50. 14, 18
51. 24, 48
52. 6, 9
53. 9, 27
54. 2, 15
55. t
56. m
57. t
58. e
59. d
60. STEP
61. LIVE
62. DEER
63. BAIL
64. GRAB
65. about
66. open
67. snap
68. faint
69. cross
70. Chairs can be made of wood.
71. wand
72. hear
73. chop
74. done
75. test
76. notice
77. nineteen
78. dated
79. hurry
80. drawer

Paper 2

1. 56, 28
2. 16, 128
3. 17, 13
4. 17, 24
5. 20, 16
6. 17
7. 3255
8. 5274
9. 7256
10. 4256
11. 5624
12. foal, calf
13. driver, pilot
14. hasten, gather
15. game, boss
16. jump, walk
17. CROSS
18. HOLIDAY
19. RULER
20. WRIST
21. PARTY
22. tip
23. skip
24. show
25. place
26. file
27. hall
28. very
29. bean
30. seat
31. rear
32. girl, mother, sweets
33. check, work, teacher
34. riding, horses, field
35. butter, sugar, eggs
36. sunny, hot, beach
37. crossroads
38. capsize
39. useless
40. seaweed
41. nearby
42. limb, crack
43. fort, party
44. play, crumbs
45. run, ideal
46. trust, shore
47. calm, still
48. beam, shine
49. scratch, graze
50. fair, honest
51. force, power
52. d
53. s
54. d
55. w
56. g
57. HIP
58. ICE
59. HOP
60. EAR
61. TOP
62–65. *Give two marks for each correct crossword.*

A	L	O	F	T
G		U		R
R	I	N	S	E
E		C		A
E	X	E	R	T

S	O	C	K	S
T		H		A
A	C	O	R	N
M		I		D
P	A	R	T	Y

66. YB, VE
67. KI, MK
68. ZEN, AFO
69. GP, ML
70. TE, FU
71. S
72. S
73. T
74. P
75. Q

Bond Verbal Reasoning Assessment Papers 10–11+ years Book 2

76 b
77 j
78 f
79 w
80 n

Paper 3

1–5 parrot C; beans B;
pine A; noodles B;
broccoli B; wren C;
willow A; robin C;
eagle C; oak A
6 clever, dull
7 divide, subtract
8 nearby, neighbouring
9 lively, sad
10 lie, complaint
11 s
12 p
13 d
14 o
15 k
16 food, healthy, body
17 giraffe, leaves, highest
18 stand, tree
19 midnight, rainy, night
20 removed, muddy, carpet
21 guilty, innocent
22 slow, swift
23 joy, sorrow
24 hazard, safety
25 accurate, wrong
26 daughter
27 twelve
28 mine
29 herd
30 Monday
31 LIFE
32 STOP
33 FIRE
34 WOOD
35 BACK
36 freeze
37 side
38 dull
39 present
40 track
41 2
42 Thomas and Charlotte
43 Kasim
44–47 *Give two marks for each correct crossword.*

N		S		A	
E	X	T	E	N	D
S		A		G	
T	I	M	B	E	R
E		P		R	
D	I	S	U	S	E

	A		P		M
I	N	S	I	D	E
	T		L		S
F	L	O	O	D	S
	E		T		E
P	R	I	S	E	D

48 SENSE
49 LINE
50 LESS
51 ? / > <
52 ? $ / < <
53 25, 33
54 9, 25
55 6, 3
56 44, 32
57 44, 69
58 model
59 mould
60 mobile
61 hold
62 nest
63 wear
64 them
65 neat
66–67 TREE, BOTTOM
68 RAIN
69–70 LIGHT, NINE
71 preen
72 dream
73 grass
74 nasty
75 honest
76 ANT
77 TEN
78 OUT
79 LAP
80 PEN

Paper 4

1 cardboard
2 myself
3 nothing
4 buttercup
5 rugby
6 PIERCE
7 FINE
8 ONCE
9 LOOSE
10 MEAN
11 spade
12 ring
13 cast
14 comfortable
15 discount
16 trainer, sock
17 hot, spicy
18 idea, drawing
19 cat, goat
20 brown, grass
21 8:45 am
22 8:15 am
23 8:05 am
24 19, 21
25 33, 18
26 3, 18
27 27, 29
28 2, 10
29 ILL
30 HAD
31 AND
32 DEN
33 ELF
34 true, false
35 rear, front
36 cheeky, polite
37 allow, deny
38 total, partial
39 k
40 b
41 w
42 k
43 t
44 Goldfish breathe underwater.
45 Bees make sweet honey.
46 Leather shoes are waterproof.
47–50 *Give two marks for each correct crossword.*

C		T		B	
H	O	R	D	E	S
E		Y		T	
E	X	I	S	T	S
K		N		E	
Y	O	G	U	R	T

G		S		R	
L	I	T	T	E	R
I		R		C	
D	R	A	W	E	R
E		I		D	
S	U	N	S	E	T

51 IS
52 OU
53 QMT
54 UW
55 SWP
56 kneeing
57 knick
58 knight
59 knead
60 kneecap
61 STORE

62 MOST
63 COURSE
64 £ @ > $
65 ? ! £ @
66 NAME, MEAN
67 SNAP, PANS
68 MILES, SLIME
69 MARCH, CHARM
70 SHAPE, PHASE
71 to, us
72 knee, cut
73 wait, sit
74 trick, were
75 cash, went
76 22
77 12
78 20
79 21
80 13

Paper 5

1 doze
2 tied
3 spot
4 bond
5 peasant
6 hit, success
7 complication, problem
8 price, fee
9 imagine, suppose
10 proof, evidence
11 steak, butcher
12 wait, playground, late
13 quiet, hear, saying
14 map, find, way
15 cities, often, buildings
16 l
17 y
18 g
19 b
20 t
21 drill
22 paddle
23 check
24 boom
25 force
26 photo
27 sauce
28 feast
29 start
30 drains
31 clap
32 plain
33 feast
34 hire
35 yearn
36 slat
37 stem
38 side
39 toad
40 noon

41 WILD
42 WITH
43 HALT
44 OVEN
45 BIND
46 still
47 dislike
48 sparse
49 welcome
50 rise
51–56 *Give two marks for each correct crossword.*

57 29, 43
58 72, 48
59 72, 45
60 10, 24
61 NJDF
62 LWOR
63 KHMD
64 PURSE
65 YOUNG
66 D
67 C
68 A
69 D
70 E
71 B
72 10
73 A D E L O P T
74 M
75 December
76 2 3 4 1
77 4 3 1 2
78 2 1 3 4
79 3 1 4 2
80 1 4 2 3

Paper 6

1 KJ, ED
2 KR, VW
3 CX, GT
4 IN, FQ
5 VU, EF
6–11 *Give two marks for each correct crossword.*

12 le
13 st
14 er
15 be
16 on
17 turn, ride, bike
18 picked, strawberries, field
19 dry, plates, cupboard
20 goggles, swim
21 complain, loud, music
22 head
23 meat
24 them
25 abundant, plentiful
26 answer, reply
27 rhythm, beat
28 alter, change
29 injury, damage
30 Raj
31 SURE

32 PURSE
33 ROPE
34 UVYW
35 HEAD
36 9
37 28
38 4
39 1
40 24
41 ARE
42 THE
43 LIP
44 RAP
45 PEN
46 assortment
47 instructor
48 outside
49 fixed
50 blend
51 PALM PALE
52 HARK HARE
53 WART WARS
54 BITE BILE
55 DAZE MAZE
56 cap, helmet
57 garden, garage
58 trying, writing
59 moon, sun
60 winter, summer
61 though, frog
62 bat, mouse
63 ray, them
64 bend, black
65 chat, least
66 OUT
67 UP
68 UNDER
69 TEA
70 POST
71 bead
72 fade
73 decade
74 café
75 face
76–79 sand B; era C;
diving B; waistcoat A;
linen A; annual C;
cliffs B; Monday C
80 Some animals live in rainforests.

Paper 7

1 PROSPECT
2 PROVOKE
3 PROVINCE
4 PROVISION
5 PROSPER
6 crisp
7 listener
8 idle
9 shorten

10 connect
11 ACT
12 ILL
13 ROW
14 OWE
15 FOR
16 l
17 f
18 p
19 h
20 c
21 far, ideal
22 chill, yearn
23 sage, stuck
24 cove, drawn
25 fed, pound
26 gpsl
27 tqppo
28 dvq
29 KNIFE
30 SAUCER
31 B
32 6752
33 2465
34 8236
35 64782
36 82465
37 courage, bravery
38 glance, look
39 halt, stop
40 cross, angry
41 tint, colour
42 brief, amazing
43 fruit, vegetable
44 listening, tasting
45 active, pity
46 fragile, squander
47 he
48 on
49 ce
50 us
51 in
52 ROBIN
53 CINEMA
54 MAGICIAN
55 CAMEL
56 COMMENCE
57 65, 36
58 24, 30
59 85, 103
60 125, 50
61 12, 16
62 SPIN
63 PIER
64 STAGE
65 CHEAT
66 TRAP
67 day, month
68 chair table
69 cheap, expensive
70 tail, claws

71 tea, water
72 was, in
73 form, each
74 from, some
75 on, up
76 made, admit
77–80 *Give two marks for each correct crossword.*

Paper 8

1 tadpole
2 kind
3 keys
4 suggest
5 export
6 WATER
7 LAND
8 DAY
9 RAIN
10 WIND
11 snowdrop
12 wail
13 soar
14 spring
15 rain
16 RAT
17 WIN
18 OUR
19 TEN
20 EAT
21–24 *Give two marks for each correct crossword.*

Grid:
	C		R		S
C	R	O	U	C	H
	E		M		I
M	A	R	B	L	E
	K		L		L
A	S	C	E	N	D

25 86253
26 25979
27 37527
28 93641
29 RAIL
30 REVEAL
31 TS, KJ
32 FR, GS
33 MH, KI
34 PT, UY
35 KO, QW
36 bleed
37 tests
38 overstay
39 ginger
40 leader
41 burnt, oven
42 Tired, sleep, school
43 dog, kennel, raining
44 question, plan, answer
45 pleased, holiday, summer
46 k
47 n
48 e
49 b
50 t
51 HAVE
52 NOSE
53 PALM
54 MOAN
55 STAR
56 DESIRE
57 DESCEND
58 DESCRIBE
59 D
60 9
61 7
62 2
63 10
64 9
65 Rings can be made of metal.
66 vague, certain
67 scatter, collect
68 satisfy, disappoint
69 undermine, enhance
70 unusual, ordinary
71 insect
72 throughout
73 nomad
74 attempt
75 beam
76 AMPYJ
77 CNKDK
78 RIGHT
79 ICUFTAY
80 BQDG

1 MENTAL, LAMENT
2 STATE, TASTE
3 REWARD, DRAWER
4 CRATE, REACT
5 STOAT, TOAST
6 amount
7 stroll
8 difficult
9 scrape
10 talent
11 TOMB
12 GROUND
13 GARDEN
14 CYPRF
15 JMUCQR
16 twin
17 keen
18 peel
19 heal
20 sour
21 open, closed
22 war, peace
23 alert, distracted
24 deliberate, accidental
25 essential, unimportant
26 flee, remain
27 mad, sane
28 Some animals in Africa feed on leaves.
29 Sounds can be represented by letters.
30–35 *Give two marks for each correct crossword.*

L	A	P
E	G	O
D	O	T

T	O	E
W	A	Y
O	R	E

D	I	P
A	C	E
M	E	T

36 6, 15
37 27, 37
38 55, 15
39 14, 22
40 28, 24
41 in
42 se
43 al
44 er
45 st
46 litre, kilogram
47 look, march
48 clear, weather
49 London, France
50 hinder, depress
51 rock
52 snappy
53 understanding
54 class
55 blossom
56 site
57 over
58 fate
59 sire
60 has
61 FADE
62 REAL
63 BRIEF
64 RAGE
65 LAPSE
66 go, cinema, week
67 autumn, leaves, fall
68 friends, play, park
69 parents, watching, television
70 clock, time, second
71 4356
72 5635
73 7254
74 6243
75 4273
76 get, stay
77 spent, saved
78 hair, teeth
79 songs, movies or films
80 hungry, thirsty

1 NH, OI
2 KZ, PU
3 ID, FF
4 FV, CY
5 MP, NO
6 husband, wife
7 unite, join
8 pig, sty
9 spirited, vigorous
10 deny, admit
11 RAN
12 ONE
13 EAR
14 PEA
15 ASK
16 21
17 4
18 17
19 0
20 5
21 s
22 l
23 h

Bond Verbal Reasoning Assessment Papers 10–11+ years Book 2

24 d
25 t
26 guest
27 limited
28 drop
29 approve
30 genuine
31 STAMP
32 PROUD
33 INVITED
34 ACCIDENT
35 PURSE

36–39 *Give two marks for each correct crossword.*

40 Some people drink Chinese tea.
41 5361
42 1537
43 2845
44 6924
45 7824
46 SEAT
47 April
48 crawl
49 grain
50 darts
51 TRAP
52 RISK
53 PAST
54 WAVE
55 RIVAL
56 share
57 thrust
58 voice
59 clean
60 swift
61 TW
62 CH
63 NS
64 QR
65 RE
66 justify, explain
67 common, ordinary
68 flood, overflow

69 stale, old
70 wreck, destroy
71 able, life
72 pot, frail
73 stale, brush
74 raft, cup
75 grin, neat
76 arrest, arrogant, artful, artificial, artistic
77 exhibit, exhilarate, exile, expand, expectancy
78 reason, reassure, rebel, rebuild, recite
79 illegible, illicit, illogical, illusion, illustrate
80 force, forcible, forecast, foreign, forever

Paper 11

1 FILE, FILL
2 FIST, MIST
3 SEAR, SEAL
4 HERB, HERD
5 LICE, VICE
6 RACE, FACE
7 pet, eat, overweight
8 travel, rocket, astronauts
9 teacher, report, improve
10 cards, cats, dog
11 NOTE
12 OVER
13 FLASH
14 BATH
15 UNDER
16 cheat
17 tale
18 sore
19 dart
20 paired
21 wail
22 than
23 best
24 mate
25 stop
26 leg
27 serious
28 outrageous
29 edge
30 reluctantly
31–34 *Give two marks for each correct crossword.*

35 5432
36 4216
37 3162
38 6145
39 1435
40 3265
41 SE, WI
42 I I, ME
43 DS, ER
44 31, 40
45 56, 61
46 negotiate, discuss
47 support, assist
48 peace, calm
49 determined, persistent
50 Tomorrow is Saturday.
51 sh
52 ma
53 gh
54 te
55 se
56 flight
57 trim
58 notice
59 draw
60 air
61 nurse, medicine
62 boredom, indifference
63 glass, cup
64 hunger, starving
65 robin, ostrich
66 ARCH
67 LOCK
68 REST
69 TURN
70 PORT
71 panting
72 pasty
73 port
74 sight
75 quit
76 DEPART, PARTED
77 REMIT, MERIT
78 SEVER, VERSE
79 RETRACE, CATERER
80 HORSE, SHORE

Paper 12

1 h
2 d
3 t

Bond Verbal Reasoning Assessment Papers 10–11+ years Book 2

4 b
5 n
6 r
7 3 4 2 1
8 1 3 4 2
9 3 1 2 4
10 C
11 6
12 16
13 11

14–17 *Give two marks for each correct crossword.*

D	E	W
O	W	E
G	E	T

S	U	M
E	R	A
E	N	D

18 XLG
19 MVZG
20 URHS
21 appear, vanish
22 variety, routine
23 ready, unprepared
24 treasured, ignored
25 Not all dogs have name tags.
26 SERVE
27 UNITE
28 NEEDS
29 THREAD
30 LAMP
31 beginning, ending
32 croaks, roars
33 maximum, heavy
34 children, women
35 trustworthy, threaten
36 EARN
37 BOIL
38 DOWN
39 TIER
40 LOFT
41 BAND
42 FORM
43 LIST
44 WARD
45 MINT
46 aeroplane, car
47 lake, harbour
48 begin, start
49 compassionate, charitable
50 rubbish, insects
51 dairy, diary
52 hits, goals
53 adults, children
54 sum, word

55 toy, pet
56 exist
57 stroke
58 value
59 weary
60 mince
61 gentle, calm
62 cold, unfriendly
63 graceful, ballerina
64 prevent, allow
65 6472
66 8342
67 2415
68 BODY
69 BREAD
70 IMB
71 YTM
72 WV
73 NUJ
74 YV
75 GI, PR
76 BX, JP
77 UF, TG
78 33, 48
79 18, 13
80 26, 32

Paper 13

1 tricky, faithful
2 reward, punishment
3 reject, accept
4 wing, paw
5 invented, actual
6 ban
7 have
8 slash
9 cave
10 path
11 reaction, response
12 spread, expand
13 fix, repair
14 degree, amount
15 hole, opening
16 15, 13
17 29, 64
18 8, 8
19 49, 64
20 20, 25
21 Claire and Amy
22 VDYH
23 OGURCIG
24 WINDY
25 Crows lay eggs.
26 st
27 te
28 me
29 pe

30 er
31 MATCH
32 HAIR
33 NIGHT
34 BACK
35 IN
36 patch
37 weak
38 in
39 ate
40 bark
41 last
42 needle
43 land
44 state
45 tough
46 risk, bowl
47 band, harm
48 fame, camel
49 boar, draw
50 ton, mean
51 PL, SI
52 CX, FU
53 UE, SG
54 MN, UV
55 6341
56 6542
57 2463
58 5736
59 order
60 drove
61 POST
62 FERN
63 EVER
64 PINE
65 SAVE
66 MEAN
67 TEAM
68 DARE
69 STAR
70 THROB

71–74 *Give two marks for each correct crossword.*

B	A	R
E	G	O
G	O	T

T	I	N
A	C	E
P	E	T

75 wolf, howl
76 grab, snatch
77 crowded, deserted
78 glass, glasses
79 damage, harm
80 wave, sea

Bond Verbal Reasoning Assessment Papers 10–11+ years Book 2

A B C D E F G H I J K L M N O P Q R S T U V W X Y Z

If the code for P L A T E is q m b u f, what are the codes for these words?

B 24

26 FORK _____

27 SPOON _____

28 CUP _____

What do these codes stand for?

29 l o j g f _____

30 t b v d f s _____

5

A, B, C, D and E are boats in a race. A is due south of C and due north west of B. D is west of A.

B 25

31 Which boat is furthest east? _____

1

Here are the number codes for four words. Match the right code to the right word.

B 24

PUSH   HOPS   CHAP   POUCH

2465   8236   6752   64782

32 PUSH _____

33 HOPS _____

34 CHAP _____

35 POUCH _____

36 Write CHOPS in code. _____

5

Underline the two words in each line which are most similar in type or meaning.

B 5

Example	dear	pleasant	poor	extravagant	expensive
37 coward	guilty	courage	bravery	tough	remedy
38 face	glance	prevent	permit	look	suggest
39 traffic	lights	halt	car	road	stop
40 cross	stingy	generous	angry	loving	wealthy
41 red	paper	paint	tint	artist	colour

5

Complete the following sentences in the best way by choosing one word from each set of brackets.

B 15

Example Tall is to (tree, short, colour) as narrow is to (thin, white, wide).

42 Short is to (shirt, maximum, brief) as incredible is to (believable, edible, amazing).

43 Pear is to (fruit, tree, pair) as cabbage is to (soup, vegetable, sprout).

44 Ear is to (ring, listening, noticed) as mouth is to (head, lips, tasting).

45 Vigorous is to (active, athlete, feeble) as sympathy is to (crying, upset, pity).

46 Tough is to (fragile, strict, harmless) as save is to (money, earn, squander).

5

Find two letters which will end the first word and start the second word.

B 10

> **Example** rea (c h) air

47 soot   (___ ___) althy

48 up   (___ ___) ce

49 offi   (___ ___) real

50 circ   (___ ___) ual

5

51 pla   (___ ___) vent

Rearrange the muddled letters in capitals to make a proper word. The answer will complete the sentence sensibly.

B 16

> **Example**   A BEZAR is an animal with stripes.   ZEBRA

52 A NORIB is a type of bird.   _____

53 Films are shown in a AMNICE.   _____

54 A GIMANIAC does tricks with cards.   _____

55 A LAECM doesn't need much water.   _____

5

56 CEMNOCME means to begin.   _____

Give the two missing numbers in the following sequences.

B 23

> **Example**   2   4   6   8   10   12

57 75   28   70   32   ___   ___   60

58 6   12   18   ___   ___   36   42

59 73   75   79   ___   93   ___   115

60 175   150   ___   100   75   ___   25

5

61 6   8   9   12   ___   ___   15

Rearrange the letters in capitals to make another word. The new word has something to do with the first two words.

B 16

> **Example**   spot soil SAINT   STAIN

62 turn   swirl   PINS   _____

63 quay   jetty   RIPE   _____

64 platform   phase   GATES   _____

65 deceive   trick   TEACH   _____

5

66 snare   catch   PART   _____

Change one word so that the sentence makes sense. Underline the word you are taking out and write your new word on the line.

Example   I waited in line to buy a <u>book</u> to see the film.   <u>ticket</u>

67 The shortest day of the year is February.   _____

68 I reserved a chair for two at the restaurant.   _____

69 Her father complained that the telephone
    bill was too cheap.   _____

70 The kitten scratched her tail on our new chair.   _____

71 She boiled just enough tea in the kettle to
    make a hot drink.   _____

5

Find and underline the two words which need to change places for each sentence to make sense.

Example   She went to <u>letter</u> the <u>write</u>.

72 Was which year in the big storm?

73 It is important that form each is filled in completely.

74 From friends some Australia are visiting.

75 We picked on shells up the beach.

76 I made that I have admit a mistake.

5

Fill in the crosswords so that all the given words are included. You have been given one letter as a clue in each crossword.

77–78

defuse, pavers, assets, cheers,
disuse, lavish

79–80

whiter, drench, bitten, search,
bother, docile

4

Now go to the Progress Chart to record your score!   Total   **80**

31

Paper 8

B 15

Complete the following expressions by underlining the missing word.

Example Frog is to tadpole as swan is to (duckling, baby, <u>cygnet</u>).

1 Butterfly is to caterpillar as frog is to (pond, tadpole, croak).

2 Vacant is to occupied as mean is to (selfish, person, kind).

3 Clock is to hands as piano is to (music, keys, instrument).

4 Fair is to just as imply is to (order, suggest, request).

5 Fact is to fiction as import is to (purchase, sell, export).

5

B 11

Find a word that can be put in front of each of the following words to make new, compound words.

Example CAST FALL WARD POUR <u>DOWN</u>

6 CRESS COLOUR FALL MELON _____

7 LADY MARK SLIDE LORD _____

8 LIGHT BREAK DREAM TIME _____

9 COAT BOW DROP FALL _____

10 FALL BURN MILL BREAK _____

5

B 1

Underline the word in the brackets which goes best with the words outside the brackets.

Example word, paragraph, sentence (pen, cap, <u>letter,</u> top, stop)

11 daffodil, poppy, tulip (stem, plant, snowdrop, grow, garden)

12 shriek, howl, roar (sound, whisper, wail, conversation, noise)

13 climb, rise, ascend (shrink, arrive, movement, soar, descend)

14 autumn, winter, summer (year, Easter, calendar, spring, season)

15 hail, sleet, snow (thunder, rain, drought, wet, weather)

5

B 22

Find the three-letter word which can be added to the letters in capitals to make a new word. The new word will complete the sentence sensibly.

Example The cat sprang onto the MO. <u>USE</u>

16 What shall we do to CELEBE your birthday? _____

17 I must stop CHEG my pencil. _____

18 The picture was very COLFUL. _____

19 My parents can both ATD Sports Day. _____

20 It's hard to BRHE whilst swimming under water. _____

5

Fill in the crosswords so that all the given words are included. You have been given one letter as a clue in each crossword.

21–22

nearer, handle, leader, savage
edited, halter

23–24

rumble, marble, creaks, ascend,
shield, crouch

4

Here are the number codes for four words. Match the right code to the right word.

RIVAL	VASES	LEAVE	SLIMY
25979	37527	93641	86253

25 RIVAL   _____

26 VASES   _____

27 LEAVE   _____

28 SLIMY   _____

Decode these numbers:

29 8563   _____

30 872753   _____

6

Give the two missing pairs of letters in the following sequences. The alphabet has been written out to help you.

A B C D E F G H I J K L M N O P Q R S T U V W X Y Z

	Example	CQ	DQ	EP	FP	_GO_	_HO_
31	ZY	WV	___	QP	NM	___	
32	CO	DP	EQ	___	___	HT	
33	UD	SE	QF	OG	___	___	
34	AE	FJ	KO	___	___	ZD	
35	BC	EG	HK	___	NS	___	

5

Underline the one word which **cannot be made** from the letters of the word in capital letters.

B 7

| | Example | STATIONERY | stone | tyres | ration | <u>nation</u> | noisy |

36 BREAKABLE   bleak   area   leer   bleed   rabble

37 POTATOES   state   tests   soap   taste   post

38 CONTROVERSY   strove   sorry   overstay   very   store

39 BELONGINGS   singe   longing   ginger   lobes   gongs

40 DREADFUL   fared   leader   flared   deaf   ladder

Complete the following sentences by selecting the most sensible word from each group of words given in the brackets. Underline the words selected.

B 14

Example   The (<u>children</u>, books, foxes) carried the (houses, <u>books</u>, steps) home from the (greengrocer, <u>library</u>, factory).

41 The cake was (burnt, frozen, ready) because she was too late removing it from the (cupboard, oven, shop).

42 (Happy, Energetic, Tired) children who don't get enough (food, sleep, drink) find it hard to concentrate at (home, play, school).

43 The (hamster, dog, horse) stayed in the (kennel, nest, den) while it was (windy, raining, playing) outside.

44 Read the (question, reply, word), then carefully (imagine, guess, plan) your (answer, problem, subject).

45 Everyone was (sad, pleased, hurt) that we had a great (holiday, birthday, marriage) that (night, season, summer).

Find the letter which will complete both pairs of words, ending the first word and starting the second. The same letter must be used for both pairs of words.

B 10

Example   mea (t) able   fi (t) ub

46 bar (___) ettle   wal (___) now

47 bea (___) est   gri (___) ose

48 fac (___) ase   sal (___) ast

49 ro (___) old   com (___) lack

50 for (___) ask   war (___) ent

Look at the first group of three words. The word in the middle has been made from the other two words. Complete the second group of three words in the same way, making a new word in the middle.

Example   PAIN INTO TOOK   ALSO <u>SOON</u> ONLY

51	BOWL	<u>BORE</u>	READ	HARD	_____	VEST
52	HINT	<u>THAW</u>	WEAK	OPEN	_____	EASY
53	TIED	<u>DONE</u>	FRONT	LIMP	_____	STALE
54	BALL	<u>WELL</u>	WEIRD	LEAN	_____	MOIST
55	PRAYS	<u>CHAP</u>	PATCH	ROAST	_____	WRIST

DESIRE   DESCRIBE   DESPAIR   DESERVE   DESCEND

If these words were placed in alphabetical order, which one would come:

56 fourth ?   _____

57 first?   _____

58 second?   _____

A B C D and E are five cars in a race.
C finishes three minutes ahead of E.
D takes fifteen minutes to complete the race, which is three minutes slower than E.
A wins the race, beating C by two minutes and B by four minutes.

59 Which car comes last?   _____

60 How many minutes does C take to complete the race?   _____

If $s = 1$, $t = 2$, $u = 3$, $v = 4$, $w = 5$ and $x = 6$, find the value of the following:

61 $(t \times u) + s =$ _____

62 $\dfrac{x}{u} =$ _____

63 $(w \times v) \div t =$ _____

64 $u \times u =$ _____

Read the first two statements and then underline one of the four options below that must be true.

65 'Gold is a metal. Rings can be made of gold.'

Rings are always made of metal.

Rings are usually made of gold.

Rings can be made of metal.

Gold is an expensive metal.

1

Underline the pair of words most opposite in meaning.

Example cup, mug coffee, milk <u>hot, cold</u>

66 vague, certain   coarse, rough   modern, new

67 fall, drop   purchase, buy   scatter, collect

68 satisfy, disappoint   scare, panic   promise, pledge

69 provide, supply   undermine, enhance   advice, recommendation

70 bronze, copper   nervous, stressed   unusual, ordinary

B 9

5

Underline two words, one from each group, that go together to form a new word. The word in the first group always comes first.

Example (hand, <u>green</u>, for)   (light, <u>house</u>, sure)

71 (out, in, wide)   (light, sect, part)

72 (through, in, though)   (sign, full, out)

73 (what, we, no)   (mad, lie, at)

74 (all, at, in)   (track, together, tempt)

75 (act, be, leg)   (for, am, all)

B 8

5

A B C D E F G H I J K L M N O P Q R S T U V W X Y Z

Solve the problems by working out the letter codes.

76 If the code for JURY is HSPW, what is the code for CORAL? _____

77 If the code for SHARP is UJCTR, what is the code for ALIBI? _____

78 If the code for PLANK is LHWJG, what does the code NECDP mean? _____

79 If the code for MINCE is NKQGJ, what is the code for HARBOUR? _____

80 If the code for FOUR is GNVQ, what is the code for ARCH? _____

B 24

5

Now go to the Progress Chart to record your score!   Total   **80**

Paper 9

Underline the two words on each line which are made from the same letters.

Example TAP   PET   <u>TEA</u>   POT   <u>EAT</u>

1 METEOR   LAMENT   TREMOR   METAL   MENTAL   LATER

2 START   TASTE   STATE   PLEAT   TRAPS   TRUST

3 REWARD   FREE   DRAFT   DRAWER   REFER   WAFER

4 TRACT   CHEAT   CRATE   ACHE   REACT   RATE

5 STOAT   OATS   STORE   TOES   ROSE   TOAST

B 7

5

36

Underline the word in the brackets closest in meaning to the word in capitals.

> **Example**   UNHAPPY   (unkind   death   laughter   <u>sad</u>   friendly)

6   QUANTITY   (ingredients   long   cooking   order   amount)

7   RAMBLE   (hiker   stroll   trail   thorn   path)

8   AWKWARD   (graceful   simple   skilful   false   difficult)

9   GRAZE   (knee   fall   scrape   plaster   skin)

10   FLAIR   (secret   lie   truth   talent   whisper)

5

A B C D E F G H I J K L M N O P Q R S T U V W X Y Z

If Z M R R M K is the code for BOTTOM what do these codes stand for?

11   R M K Z   _____

12   E P M S L B   _____

13   E Y P B C L   _____

What are the codes for the following words?

14   EARTH   _____

15   LOWEST   _____

5

Find the four-letter word hidden at the end of one word and the beginning of the next word. The order of the letters may not be changed.

> **Example**   The children had bats and balls.   <u>*sand*</u>

16   The team did not win a match this year.   _____

17   I hope we can make enough cakes for next Sunday's cake sale.   _____

18   I do hope eleven pounds isn't too much to spend.   _____

19   She always helps out when needed.   _____

20   Money is also urgently needed by the charity.   _____

5

Underline the two words, one from each group, which are the most opposite in meaning.

> **Example**   (dawn, <u>early</u>, awake)   (<u>late</u>, stop, sunrise)

21   (open, shut, near)   (closed, almost, stop)

22   (trip, war, down)   (battle, fall, peace)

23   (alert, bright, perfect)   (awake, distracted, clever)

24   (deliberate, aim, hostile)   (accidental, unfriendly, planned)

25   (secret, essential, locate)   (discover, find, unimportant)

26   (flee, weekend, busy)   (remain, walk, wander)

27   (happy, mad, complete)   (sane, whole, joyful)

7

Read the first two statements and then underline one of the four options below that must be true.

B 25

28 'Many mammals are plant-eaters. Some mammals live in Africa.'

Some mammals live in herds.

Many plants are found only in Africa.

Some animals in Africa feed on leaves.

Most of the animals in Africa are mammals.

Read the first two statements and then underline one of the four options below that must be true.

29 'Language is based on words. Letters are used for each sound in a word.'

Words are usually written.

Sounds can be represented by letters.

There are many different languages.

All languages use the same alphabet.

2

Fill in the crosswords so that all the given words are included. You have been given one letter as a clue in each crossword.

B 19

30–31
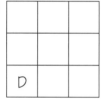

lap, pot, ego,
dot, led, ago

32–33
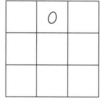

two, oar, eye,
way, ore, toe

34–35

dam, ice, pet,
ace, met, dip

6

Give the two missing numbers in the following sequences.

B 23

	Example	2	4	6	8	<u>10</u>	<u>12</u>
36	3	___	9	12	___	18	21
37	7	9	13	19	___	___	49
38	___	42	31	22	___	10	7
39	6	___	___	30	38	46	54
40	14	36	21	30	___	___	35

5

Find two letters which will end the first word and start the second word.

B 10

Example   rea (<u>c h</u>) air

41 cha   (___ ___) vade

42 cau   (___ ___) rious

43 norm   (___ ___) ways

44 rememb   (___ ___) ror

45 toa   (___ ___) reet

5

Underline the two words which are the odd ones out in the following groups of words.

Example   black   <u>king</u>   purple   green   <u>house</u>

46 metre   litre   centimetre   kilometre   kilogram

47 shout   look   whisper   march   talk

48 dull   clear   boring   unexciting   weather

49 London   city   country   France   town

50 promote   encourage   hinder   boost   depress

Underline the one word in the brackets which will go equally well with both the pairs of words outside the brackets.

Example   rush, attack   cost, fee   (price, hasten, strike, <u>charge</u>, money)

51 stone, pebble   sway, wobble   (danger, rock, roll, hard, rough)

52 irritable, cross   brisk, lively   (touchy, sluggish, quick, snappy, hasty)

53 idea, knowledge   agreement, pact   (intelligence, understanding, cooperation, patient, acceptance)

54 division, group   grade, course   (collection, student, class, teacher, sort)

55 bud, flower   grow, progress   (plant, increase, movement, stem, blossom)

Change the first word of the third pair in the same way as the other pairs to give a new word.

Example   bind, hind   bare, hare   but, <u>hut</u>

56 bit, bite   kit, kite   sit,   _____

57 chill, hill   shops, hops   cover,   _____

58 deed, feed   dish, fish   date,   _____

59 file, life   dire, ride,   rise,   _____

60 moth, hot   with, hit   mash,   _____

Rearrange the letters in capitals to make another word. The new word has something to do with the first two words.

Example   spot, soil   SAINT   <u>STAIN</u>

61 dull, dim   DEAF   _____

62 genuine, true   EARL   _____

63 short, quick   FIBRE   _____

64 violent, fury   GEAR   _____

65 mistake, oversight   SEPAL   _____

Complete the following sentences by selecting the most sensible word from each group of words given in the brackets. Underline the words selected.

Example   The (<u>children</u>, books, foxes) carried the (houses, <u>books</u>, steps) home from the (greengrocer, <u>library</u>, factory).

66 We will (go, leave, listen) to the (cinema, holiday, moon) next (evening, week, day).

67 As (autumn, spring, winter) came the (leaves, petals, branches) began to (grow, develop, fall) from the trees.

68 You can take some (friends, money, clothes) to (play, spend, wear) with in the (bank, park, bath).

69 My (pets, parents, toys) go to bed after (watching, playing, counting) the (road, books, television).

70 A (clock, thermometer, radio) measures (temperature, time, sound) to the nearest (week, wave, second).

5

Here are the number codes for four words. Match the right code to the right word.

PEAR	AREA	SOAP	ROPE
7254	6243	4356	5635

71 PEAR   _____

72 AREA   _____

73 SOAP   _____

74 ROPE   _____

75 Write POSE in code.   _____

5

Change one word so that the sentence makes sense. Underline the word you are taking out and write your new word on the line.

Example   I waited in line to buy a <u>book</u> to see the film.   *ticket*

76 As it's Saturday tomorrow, you can get up late to watch the film.   _____

77 She spent her pocket money because she couldn't find anything tempting to buy.   _____

78 Brush your hair after eating so many sweets.   _____

79 Our cinema doesn't always show the most recent songs.   _____

80 She took a sip of her drink because she was hungry.   _____

5

Paper 10

Give the two missing pairs of letters in the following sequences. The alphabet has been written out to help you.

B 23

A B C D E F G H I J K L M N O P Q R S T U V W X Y Z

Example	CQ	DQ	EP	FP	<u>GO</u>	<u>HO</u>
1 JD	KE	LF	MG	___	___	
2 AJ	BI	DG	GD	___	___	
3 UB	PB	LD	___	GF	___	
4 HT	GU	___	EW	DX	___	
5 GV	HU	JS	KR	___	___	

5

Choose two words, one from each set of brackets, to complete the sentences in the best way.

B 15

> **Example** Smile is to happiness as (drink, <u>tear</u>, shout) is to (whisper, laugh, <u>sorrow</u>).

6 Uncle is to aunt as (husband, son, father) is to (grandmother, relative, wife).

7 Reveal is to show as (unite, copy, glance) is to (write, join, divide).

8 Lion is to den as (mouse, pig, bee) is to (stable, sty, sting).

9 Sad is to melancholy as (ghostly, spirited, lazy) is to (vigorous, calm, spiteful).

10 Depart is to arrive as (deny, agree, accept) is to (state, respond, admit).

5

Find the three-letter word which can be added to the letters in capitals to make a new word. The new word will complete the sentence sensibly.

B 22

> **Example** The cat sprang onto the MO. <u>USE</u>

11 You can ARGE to have a friend to play next week. ___

12 She felt LLY once the other children had gone home. ___

13 The answer was explained CLLY. ___

14 Mum, Danika keeps RETING what I say! ___

15 The Halloween MS scared the younger children. ___

5

If a = 6, b = 2, c = 0, d = 5, e = 10, find the answer to these calculations:

B 26

16 $a + d + e =$ ___

17 $(be) \div d =$ ___

18 $(a \times b) + d =$ ___

19 $abc =$ ___

20 $(d \times e) \div (b \times d) =$ ___

5

Which one letter can be added to the front of all of these words to make new words?

B 12

Example $\underline{c}$are $\underline{c}$at $\underline{c}$rate $\underline{c}$all

21 ____eek   ____ick   ____core   ____elf   ____ack

22 ____oyal   ____ure   ____uck   ____ist   ____oad

23 ____ook   ____oot   ____orn   ____our   ____ost

24 ____ire   ____ice   ____eed   ____eal   ____ale

25 ____oad   ____ool   ____ent   ____ank   ____uck

○ 5

Underline one word in the brackets which is most opposite in meaning to the word in capitals.

B 6

Example WIDE   (broad   vague   long   <u>narrow</u>   motorway)

26 HOST   (party   hostess   invite   guest   speak)

27 ENDLESS   (close   beginning   limited   boundary   outcome)

28 CATCH   (game   grab   try   drop   problem)

29 OBJECT   (article   focus   purpose   approve   plan)

30 ARTIFICIAL   (false   reliable   fake   genuine   environment)

○ 5

Rearrange the muddled letters in capitals to make a proper word. The answer will complete the sentence sensibly.

B 16

Example A BEZAR is an animal with stripes.   ZEBRA

31 Put a ATPMS on that before you post it!   _____

32 His mother was ODUPR of his achievements.   _____

33 I have ITENIVD everyone to my party.   _____

34 The witness described the DICTENAC.   _____

35 I lost my SERPU outside the bank.   _____

○ 5

Fill in the crosswords so that all the given words are included. You have been given one letter as a clue in each crossword.

B 19

36–37
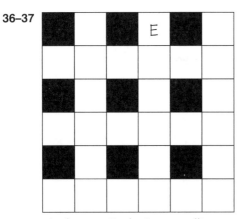

stodgy, matted, storey, editor, impart, amidst

38–39
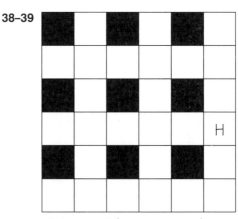

states, crutch, course, archer, censor, loiter

○ 4

42

Read the first two statements and then underline one of the four options below that must be true.

40 'Tea is grown in China. Many people drink tea.'

      Most people in China grow tea plants.

      Tea is a more popular drink than coffee.

      Some people drink Chinese tea.

      Tea is a hot drink.

Here are the number codes for four words. Match the right code to the right word.

EAST	TEAM	LIKE	SULK
6924	1537	5361	2845

41 EAST   _____

42 TEAM   _____

43 LIKE   _____

44 SULK   _____

45 Write MILK in code.   _____

46 Decode 6531.   _____

Poppy's birthday is in the month which ends with the 20th letter of the alphabet. Her brother's birthday is eight months later.

47 In which month is Poppy's brother's birthday?   _____

Underline the one word which **can be made** from the letters of the word in capital letters.

	Example	CHAMPION	camping	notch	peach	cramp	<u>chimp</u>
48	CAULIFLOWER		lions	fault	relay	colder	crawl
49	FLAVOURING		reign	vowel	gravel	grain	float
50	STRAINED		timed	darts	stripe	earl	nested

Look at the first group of three words. The word in the middle has been made from the other two words. Complete the second group of three words in the same way, making a new word in the middle.

	Example	PA<u>IN</u>	INTO	<u>TO</u>OK	ALSO	<u>SOON</u>	ONLY
51	LEND	DONE	ALSO	SPAT	_____	FOUR
52	ROSE	LOSE	SOUL	MILK	_____	SOAR
53	KIND	DICE	LACE	WASP	_____	MIST
54	PEAK	PEAT	MEAT	WAIT	_____	HIVE
55	WROTE	LOWER	RELAY	VEINS	_____	LARCH

Add one letter to the word in capital letters to make a new word. The meaning of the new word is given in the clue.

B 12

Example   PLAN   simple   _plain_

56 HARE   split, divide   _____

57 TRUST   drive, force   _____

58 VICE   human sound   _____

59 CLAN   washed   _____

60 SIFT   rapid   _____

5

Fill in the missing letters. The alphabet has been written out to help you.

B 23

A B C D E F G H I J K L M N O P Q R S T U V W X Y Z

Example   AB is to CD as PQ is to RS

61 CF is to EH as RU is to   _____

62 VX is to UY as DG is to   _____

63 TW is to VZ as LP is to   _____

64 JK is to HI as ST is to   _____

65 SW is to VU as OG is to   _____

5

Underline the two words, one from each group, which are closest in meaning.

B 3

Example   (race, shop, start)   (finish, begin, end)

66 (justify, question, right)   (legal, explain, penalty)

67 (rare, common, unusual)   (sense, real, ordinary)

68 (tap, liquid, flood)   (drought, overflow, trickle)

69 (stale, processed, cooked)   (raw, old, fresh)

70 (mess, lose, wreck)   (destroy, ship, save)

5

Move one letter from the first word and add it to the second word to make two new words.

B 13

Example   hunt   sip   _hut_   _snip_

71 fable   lie   _____   _____

72 port   fail   _____   _____

73 stable   rush   _____   _____

74 craft   up   _____   _____

75 grain   net   _____   _____

5

Write these words in alphabetical order.

76 artificial   artistic   artful   arrogant   arrest

_____ _____ _____ _____ _____

77 expand   exhilarate   expectancy   exile   exhibit

_____ _____ _____ _____ _____

78 recite   rebel   reason   reassure   rebuild

_____ _____ _____ _____ _____

79 illusion   illegible   illogical   illicit   illustrate

_____ _____ _____ _____ _____

80 foreign   forcible   forever   forecast   force

_____ _____ _____ _____ _____

5

Now go to the Progress Chart to record your score!   **Total** **80**

Paper 11

Change the first word into the last word by changing one letter at a time and making two new, different words in the middle.

Example   TEAK   <u>TEAT</u>   <u>TENT</u>   RENT

1 FIRE   _____   _____   FALL

2 FISH   _____   _____   MUST

3 NEAR   _____   _____   SELL

4 KERB   _____   _____   HARD

5 LACE   _____   _____   VILE

6 RICE   _____   _____   FACT

6

Complete the following sentences by selecting the most sensible word from each group of words given in the brackets. Underline the words selected.

Example   The (<u>children</u>, books, foxes) carried the (houses, <u>books</u>, steps) home from the (greengrocer, <u>library</u>, factory).

7 It's important to make sure that your (customer, visitor, pet) doesn't (drink, eat, work) too much and become (lazy, overweight, bossy).

8 People who (travel, shop, listen) through space in a (computer, TV, rocket) are called (hikers, astronauts, dreamers).

9 Tom's (friend, teacher, mother) wrote in his (card, invitation, report) that he must (learn, improve, spell) his handwriting.

10 Most of her birthday (presents, cake, cards) showed pictures of (cats, candles, toys), but her favourite animal is actually a (doll, dog, drawing).

4

Find a word that can be put in front of each of the following words to make new, compound words.

Example	CAST	FALL	WARD	POUR	<u>DOWN</u>
11 PAD	BOOK	PAPER	WORTHY		
12 COME	CAST	ALL	GROWN		
13 BACK	BULB	CARD	LIGHT		
14 ROOM	ROBE	TUB	WATER		
15 STANDING	LINE	GROUND	FOOT		

 5

Find a word that is similar in meaning to the word in capital letters and that rhymes with the second word.

Example	CABLE	tyre	<u>wire</u>
16 SWINDLE	beat		
17 STORY	sail		
18 PAINFUL	moor		
19 ARROW	heart		
20 MATCHED	cared		

 5

Change the first word of the third pair in the same way as the other pairs to give a new word.

Example	bind, hind	bare, hare	but, <u>hut</u>
21 tall, tail	fall, fail	wall,	
22 risk, skin	wish, shin	bath,	
23 net, nest	pet, pest	bet,	
24 gape, page	dame, made	tame,	
25 mare, ream	name, mean	post,	

 5

Complete the following expressions by underlining the missing word.

Example Frog is to tadpole as swan is to (duckling, baby, <u>cygnet</u>).

26 Wrist is to arm as ankle is to (foot, leg, toe).

27 Pleased is to delighted as solemn is to (tired, frightened, serious).

28 Sour is to sugary as reasonable is to (sensible, outrageous, thoughtful).

29 Fee is to cost as margin is to (paper, book, edge).

30 Clamour is to silence as readily is to (promptly, reluctantly, actually).

 5

46

Fill in the crosswords so that all the given words are included. You have been given one letter as a clue in each crossword.

B 19

31–32

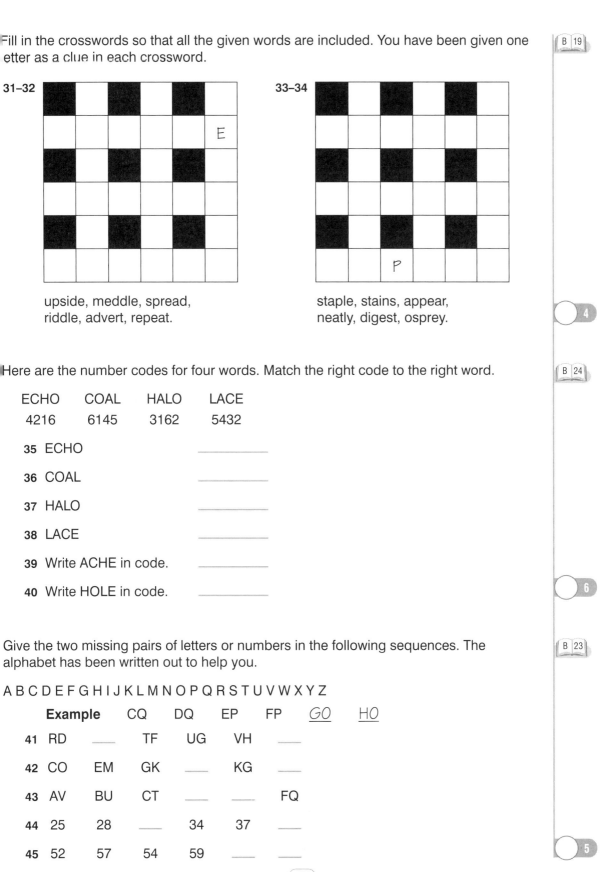

upside, meddle, spread,
riddle, advert, repeat.

33–34

staple, stains, appear,
neatly, digest, osprey.

4

Here are the number codes for four words. Match the right code to the right word.

B 24

ECHO	COAL	HALO	LACE
4216	6145	3162	5432

35 ECHO _____

36 COAL _____

37 HALO _____

38 LACE _____

39 Write ACHE in code. _____

40 Write HOLE in code. _____

6

Give the two missing pairs of letters or numbers in the following sequences. The alphabet has been written out to help you.

B 23

A B C D E F G H I J K L M N O P Q R S T U V W X Y Z

Example	CQ	DQ	EP	FP	_GO_	_HO_
41 RD	___	TF	UG	VH	___	
42 CO	EM	GK	___	KG	___	
43 AV	BU	CT	___	___	FQ	
44 25	28	___	34	37	___	
45 52	57	54	59	___	___	

5

Underline the pair of words most similar in meaning.

Example   come, go   <u>roam, wander</u>   fear, fare

46 attach, unfasten   near, distant   negotiate, discuss

47 waited, walked   support, assist   rapidly, slowly

48 peace, calm   help, ignore   cost, purse

49 graceful, clumsy   gradual, immediate   determined, persistent

4

Read the first two statements and then underline one of the four options below that must be true.

50 'Kumiko often goes to French Club on Saturday morning. Yesterday was Thursday.'

   Kumiko enjoys learning French.

   Kumiko is going to French Club today.

   Tomorrow is Saturday.

   French Club lasts for two hours.

1

Find two letters which will end the first word and start the second word.

Example   rea (<u>c h</u>) air

51 ma   (—— ——) elf

52 dra   (—— ——) nage

53 enou (—— ——) ost

54 priva (—— ——) lephone

55 plea   (—— ——) cond

5

Underline the one word in the brackets which will go equally well with both the pairs of words outside the brackets.

Example   rush, attack   cost, fee   (price, hasten, strike, <u>charge</u>, money)

56 transport, aviation   exit, fleeing   (soaring, escape, trip, flight, aeroplane)

57 slim, slender   prune, crop   (neat, trim, compact, tidy, smart)

58 advert, flyer   observe, see   (paper, notice, look, read, say)

59 tie, stalemate   trace, sketch   (raffle, trace, skill, draw, prize)

60 express, show   ventilate, freshen   (appear, disclose, space, air, expose)

5

Underline the two words which are the odd ones out in the following groups of words.

B 4

Example   black   <u>king</u>   purple   green   <u>house</u>

61 disease   fever   nurse   infection   medicine

62 curiosity   involvement   boredom   concern   indifference

63 coffee   glass   cider   cup   milk

64 eat   chew   hunger   starving   munch

65 wings   robin   beak   ostrich   talon

5

Find the four-letter word which can be added to the letters in capitals to make a new word. The new word will complete the sentence sensibly.

B 22

Example   They enjoyed the BCAST.   _ROAD_

66 The bird was kept busy SEING for food and protecting the nest.   _____

67 The truck BED the road so no one could pass.   _____

68 He watched a very INTEING programme about dinosaurs.   _____

69 I REED the book to the library on time.   _____

70 It is IMANT to protect your skin when the sun is strong.   _____

5

Remove one letter from the word in capital letters to leave a new word. The meaning of the new word is given in the clue.

B 12

Example   AUNT   an insect   _ant_

71 PAINTING   breathless   _____

72 PASTRY   small pie   _____

73 SPORT   harbour   _____

74 SLIGHT   glimpse   _____

75 QUIET   give up   _____

5

Underline the two words which are made from the same letters.

B 7

Example   TAP   PET   <u>TEA</u>   POT   <u>EAT</u>

76 REPEAT   TRAPPED   DEPART   TAPER   PARTED   DRAPE

77 DIME   MERIT   TIMED   METRE   REMIT   TREMOR

78 SEVER   SIEVE   SEVEN   VERSE   VEINS   NEVER

79 RETRACT   TRACER   RETRACE   CATERER   TRACTOR   REACT

80 HOSES   SHORT   HORSE   HORNS   SHOTS   SHORE

5

Now go to the Progress Chart to record your score!   **Total**   **80**

Paper 12

B 10

Find the letter which will complete both pairs of words, ending the first word and starting the second. The same letter must be used for both pairs of words.

Example   mea (t) able   fit (t) ub

1 batc (____) eap   pitc (____) eave

2 dee (____) amp   fon (____) eter

3 mal (____) ask   fac (____) usk

4 clu (____) lunt   cra (____) rim

5 eve (____) eon   wea (____) oble

6 stai (____) oam   flou (____) ent

6

B 20

Spell the following words backwards. Write numbers underneath the words to indicate their new alphabetical order.

7 INVISIBLE	IMPOSSIBLE	INEDIBLE	BUBBLE
_____	_____	_____	_____

8 JUICE	BRUISE	CRUISE	NUISANCE
_____	_____	_____	_____

9 HOPING	MAKING	WAKING	DRIVING
_____	_____	_____	_____

3

B 25

Five friends, A, B, C, D and E are in a queue to buy tickets at the cinema.

A is not at the back of the queue and has one person in front of him.

E has three people ahead of him, and is standing in front of D.

B is at the front of the queue.

10 Which person is in the middle of the queue?   _____

1

A B C D E F G H I J K L M N O P Q R S T U V W X Y Z

B 26

If A = 1, B = 2, C = 3 and so on, find the value of the following words by adding the letters together.

11 CAB   _____

12 CAGE   _____

13 BED   _____

3

Fill in the crosswords so that all the given words are included. You have been given one letter as a clue in each crossword.

14–15

		W

wet, ewe, dog,
get, owe, dew

16–17

E		

era, urn, mad,
see, end, sum

4

A B C D E F G H I J K L M N O P Q R S T U V W X Y Z

The code for COUNT is XLFMG what are the codes for these words:

18 COT _____

19 NEAT _____

20 FISH _____

3

Underline the two words, one from each group, which are the most opposite in meaning.

Example   (dawn, <u>early</u>, wake)   (<u>late</u>, stop, sunrise)

21 (light, appear, view)   (scenery, glow, vanish)

22 (type, sort, variety)   (assortment, routine, different)

23 (ready, easily, gladly)   (eager, unprepared, willingly)

24 (fee, jewel, treasured)   (rich, ignored, cheap)

4

Read the first two statements and then underline one of the four options below that must be true.

25 'Most dogs wear a collar. Some collars have a name tag.'

All pets wear name tags.

Some dogs without collars might get lost.

Not all dogs have name tags.

Name tags are sold in pet shops.

1

Rearrange the muddled letters in capitals to make a proper word. The answer will complete the sentence sensibly.

Example   A BEZAR is an animal with stripes.   <u>ZEBRA</u>

26 The waiter will VERSE the coffee. _____

27 Let us UNTIE our forces. _____

28 Cameron DENSE to pass his swimming test. _____

29 Can you DEARTH the cotton through the needle? _____

30 Turn off the PALM before you go to sleep. _____

5

Complete the following sentences in the best way by choosing one word from each set of brackets.

B 15

Example Tall is to (tree, <u>short</u>, colour) as narrow is to (thin, white, <u>wide</u>).

31 First is to (early, number, beginning) as last is to (only, single, ending).

32 Frog is to (croaks, green, pond) as lion is to (cub, roars, kills).

33 Minimum is to (bad, least, maximum) as light is to (weight, heavy, load).

34 Child is to (children, play, school) as woman is to (dress, women, husband).

35 Dishonest is to (false, wrong, trustworthy) as protect is to (barrier, threaten, careful).

Look at the first group of three words. The word in the middle has been made from the other two words. Complete the second group of three words in the same way, making a new word in the middle.

B 18

Example	PAIN	INTO	TOOK	ALSO	<u>SOON</u>	ONLY
36 PINT	NAIL	PALE		TREE	_____	TANK
37 RAMP	ROAM	BOAT		BULL	_____	COIN
38 PURE	WIRE	WISP		YAWN	_____	DOTE
39 CLOAK	MOLE	MODEL		WEIGH	_____	THIRD
40 WEAN	SAFE	SELF		STOP	_____	LEAF

Find the four-letter word which can be added to the letters in capitals to make a new word. The new word will complete the sentence sensibly.

B 22

Example They enjoyed the BCAST. <u>ROAD</u>

41 The wrecked car was AONED in the field. _____

42 Parents will be INED as soon as a decision is made. _____

43 Drive carefully past CYCS. _____

44 REING children for good behaviour is important. _____

45 They played BADON in the garden during the holiday. _____

Underline the two words which are the odd ones out in the following groups of words.

B 4

Example	black	<u>king</u>	purple	green	<u>house</u>
46 aeroplane	pilot	car	mechanic	engineer
47 lake	valley	plain	harbour	mountain
48 begin	suspend	terminate	start	discontinue
49 spiteful	cruel	compassionate	nasty	charitable
50 litter	rubbish	herd	insects	swarm

Change one word so that the sentence makes sense. Underline the word you are taking out and write your new word on the line.

B 14

Example   I waited in line to buy a <u>book</u> to see the film.   _ticket_

51   Writing in a dairy is a good way to remember special occasions.   _____

52   When you are playing football, the aim is to score as many hits as possible.   _____

53   Do not leave very young adults unsupervised with a dog.   _____

54   You can use your dictionary to find out what a sum means.   _____

55   A guinea pig is a small animal, often kept as a toy.   _____

◯ 5

Add one letter to the word in capital letters to make a new word. The meaning of the new word is given in the clue.

B 12

Example   PLAN   simple   _plain_

56   EXIT   to be alive   _____

57   STOKE   pat gently   _____

58   VALE   worth   _____

59   WARY   tired   _____

60   MINE   cut into small pieces   _____

◯ 5

Choose two words, one from each set of brackets, to complete the sentences in the best way.

B 15

Example   Smile is to happiness as (drink, <u>tear</u>, shout) is to (whisper, laugh, <u>sorrow</u>).

61   Ideal is to perfect as (genuine, gentle, generous) is to (common, capable, calm).

62   Immense is to enormous as (cold, shivery, chilled) is to (hot, unfriendly, pleasant).

63   Sporty is to athlete as (clumsy, graceful, heavy) is to (plumber, ballerina, chef).

64   Ignore is to notice as (prevent, perform, plunge) is to (allow, check, block).

◯ 4

Here are the number codes for three words. Match the right code to the right word.

B 24

DEFY   OBEY   YEAR
8342   6472   2415

65   DEFY   _____

66   OBEY   _____

67   YEAR   _____

Decode these numbers using the same code.

68   3862   _____

69   35416   _____

◯ 5

Fill in the missing letters. The alphabet has been written out to help you.

B 23

A B C D E F G H I J K L M N O P Q R S T U V W X Y Z

Example   AB is to CD as PQ is to _RS_

70 CXG is to DWH as HNA is to   _____

71 HEQ is to JGS as WRK is to   _____

72 BC is to YX as DE is to   _____

73 JFC is to IEB as OVK is to   _____

74 AD is to ZW as BE is to   _____

5

Give the two missing pairs of letters or numbers in the following sequences. The alphabet has been written out to help you.

B 23

A B C D E F G H I J K L M N O P Q R S T U V W X Y Z

Example   CQ   DQ   EP   FP   _GO_   _HO_

75	AC	DF	___	JL	MO	___
76	___	DV	FT	HR	___	LN
77	VE	___	___	SH	RI	QJ
78	3	6	12	21	___	___
79	19	15	___	14	17	___
80	2	8	14	20	___	___

6

Now go to the Progress Chart to record your score!   Total   **80**

Paper 13

Complete the following sentences in the best way by choosing one word from each set of brackets.

B 15

Example   Tall is to (tree, <u>short</u>, colour) as narrow is to (thin, white, <u>wide</u>).

1 Complicated is to (wicked, tricky, straightforward) as loyal is to (faithful, difficult, awkward).

2 Prize is to (certificate, badge, reward) as penalty is to (punishment, gift, payment).

3 Exclude is to (allow, school, reject) as include is to (refuse, accept, destroy).

4 Bat is to (ball, wing, cricket) as rabbit is to (grass, hop, paw).

5 Imaginary is to (mind, possible, invented) as real is to (actual, copy, fake).

5

Remove one letter from the word in capital letters to leave a new word. The meaning of the new word is given in the clue.

B 12

    Example   AUNT   an insect   <u>ant</u>

6 BEAN   forbid   _____

7 HALVE   possess   _____

8 SPLASH   cut   _____

9 CARVE   hole under the ground   _____

5

10 PATCH   course of action   _____

Underline the two words, one from each group, which are closest in meaning.

B 3

    Example   (race, shop, <u>start</u>)   (finish, <u>begin</u>, end)

11 (behave, reaction, move)   (response, look, knowledge)

12 (shorten, spread, lessen)   (traffic, expand, carry)

13 (arrange, definite, fix)   (harm, repair, vary)

14 (degree, lesser, deliberate)   (college, mistake, amount)

5

15 (spot, nest, hole)   (filling, opening, round)

Give the two missing numbers in the following sequences.

B 23

    Example   CQ   DQ   EP   FP   <u>GO</u>   <u>HO</u>

16 9   7   12   10   ___   ___   18

17 22   ___   36   43   50   57   ___

18 2   4   4   ___   6   12   ___

19 9   16   25   36   ___   ___   81

5

20 10   15   ___   ___   30   35   40

Claire and Amy are studying Science and Maths, and Harry and Fred study History and Geography.

B 25

Jacob and Henry like Art and Spanish, but Amelia's worst subject is French.

Ravi does Maths, but no longer has Geography lessons.

All the girls do Drama.

21 Which children are learning more than two subjects? _____

1

A B C D E F G H I J K L M N O P Q R S T U V W X Y Z

Solve the problems by working out the letter codes.

B 24

22 If the code for SOUP is VRXS, what is the code for SAVE? _____

23 If the code for FOLDER is HMNBGP, what is the code for MISTAKE? _____

24 If the code for BRAKE is DUEPK, what does the code YLRIE mean? _____

3

Read the first two statements and then underline one of the four options below that must be true.

25 'Crows and magpies are birds. Birds lay eggs.'

      Magpies are black and white.

      Crows lay eggs.

      Many crows and magpies share nests.

      Nests are only used for laying eggs.

1

Find two letters which will end the first word and start the second word.

    Example   rea (c h) air

26 almo   (__ __) art

27 exci   (__ __) mper

28 fra   (__ __) lon

29 sha   (__ __) rmit

30 whisp (__ __) upt

5

Find a word that can be put in front of each of the following words to make new, compound words.

    Example   CAST   FALL   WARD   POUR   <u>DOWN</u>

31 BOX   STICK   PLAY   MAKER   _____

32 BRUSH   CUT   SPRAY   STYLE   _____

33 CLUB   DRESS   MARE   FALL   _____

34 TRACK   WATER   LOG   YARD   _____

35 COME   CORRECT   CREASE   DIRECT   _____

5

Change the first word of the third pair in the same way as the other pairs to give a new word.

    Example   bind, hind   bare, hare   but, <u>hut</u>

36 hat, hatch   mat, match   pat,   _____

37 bake, beak   lake, leak   wake,   _____

38 trust, us   clamp, am   bring,   _____

39 base, sea   fear, are   seat,   _____

40 line, link   tale, talk   bare,   _____

5

Underline the one word in the brackets which will go equally well with both the pairs of words outside the brackets.

Example   rush, attack   cost, fee   (price, hasten, strike, <u>charge</u>, money)

41 final, latest   continue, go on   (remain, last, cease, behind, proceed)

42 thorn, quill   annoy, pester   (tease, stick, needle, stem, poke)

43 earth, ground   arrive, come down   (planet, rest, soil, land, run)

44 explain, say   condition, phase   (report, shape, state, situation, express)

45 strong, firm   stern, strict   (solid, gentle, kind, healthy, tough)

5

Move one letter from the first word and add it to the second word to make two new words.

Example   hunt sip   _hut_   _snip_

46 brisk   owl   _____   _____

47 brand   ham   _____   _____

48 flame   came   _____   _____

49 board   raw   _____   _____

50 tone   man   _____   _____

5

Give the two missing pairs of letters in the following sequences. The alphabet has been written out to help you.

A B C D E F G H I J K L M N O P Q R S T U V W X Y Z

Example   CQ   DQ   EP   FP   _GO_   _HO_

51   DX   GU   JR   MO   ___   ___

52   BY   ___   DW   EV   ___   GT

53   WC   UE   VD   TF   ___   ___

54   ___   OP   QR   ST   ___   WX

4

Here are the number codes for four words. Match the right code to the right word.

ROAD   REAL   DARE   OVER
5736   2463   6341   6542

55 REAL   _____

56 ROAD   _____

57 DARE   _____

58 OVER   _____

Decode these numbers using the same code.

59 56236   _____

60 26573   _____

6

Look at the first group of three words. The word in the middle has been made from the other two words. Complete the second group of three words in the same way, making a new word in the middle.

B 18

		Example	PAIN	INTO	TOOK	ALSO	<u>SOON</u>	ONLY

61	ARMY	RACE	CHEW		OPEN	_____	SITS
62	SLAP	PALM	HELM		REEF	_____	BARN
63	CHIRP	RICE	PRICE		ELDER	_____	DIVER
64	REIN	NOTE	OTTER		REAP	_____	INCH
65	GAME	ROAM	BORE		OVEN	_____	FAST

5

Rearrange the letters in capitals to make another word. The new word has something to do with the first two words.

B 16

	Example	spot, soil	SAINT	<u>STAIN</u>
66	unkind, nasty		NAME	_____
67	players, game		MEAT	_____
68	brave, challenge		READ	_____
69	celebrity, twinkling light		RATS	_____
70	vibrate, thump		BROTH	_____

5

Fill in the crosswords so that all the given words are included. You have been given one letter as a clue in each crossword.

B 19

71–72

got, ego, bar,
ago, rot, beg

73–74

ace, net, tap,
ice, pet, tin

4

Choose two words, one from each set of brackets, to complete the sentences in the best way.

B 15

Example Smile is to happiness as (drink, <u>tear</u>, shout) is to (whisper, laugh, <u>sorrow</u>).

75 Bee is to buzz as (pig, wolf, duck) is to (piglet, lake, howl).

76 Rear is to back as (grab, give, punch) is to (hold, snatch, kick).

77 Crude is to polite as (pile, crowded, sandy) is to (crushed, demolished, deserted).

78 Leaf is to leaves as (cup, eyesight, glass) is to (water, glasses, mugs).

79 Tease is to irritate as (damage, assist, know) is to (harm, ignore, repair).

80 Star is to sky as (sail, wave, greeting) is to (friendly, land, sea).

6

Now go to the Progress Chart to record your score! Total

80

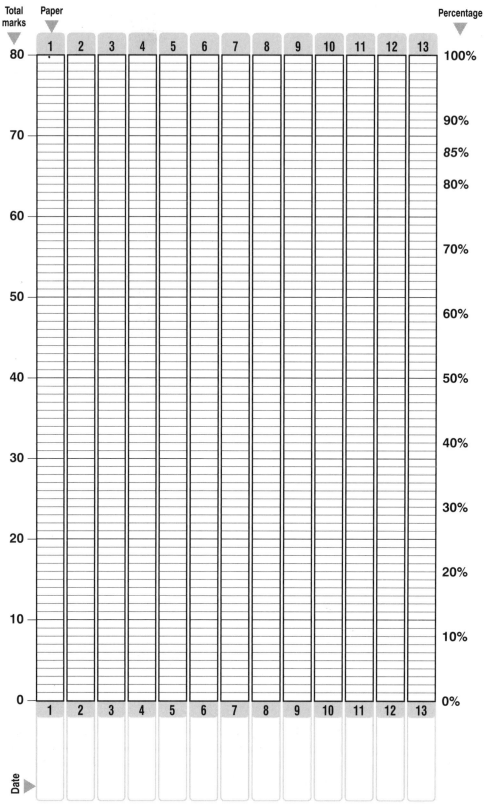

When you've finished the book use the Next Steps Planner